Truth and Consequences

by MIRIAM YOUNG

Illustrated by Diane de Groat

SCHOLASTIC BOOK SERVICES

NEW YORK • TORONTO • LONDON • AUCKLAND • SYDNEY • TOKYO

A hardcover edition of this book is published by Four Winds Press, a division of Scholastic, and is available through your local bookstore or directly from Four Winds Press, 50 West 44th St., New York, N.Y. 10036.

ISBN: 0-590-04555-5

13 12 11 10 9 8 7 6 5 4 3   0 1 2 3/8

Truth and
Consequences

Chapter 1

WE ALL KNOW that telling lies gets you in trouble. So telling the truth ought to keep you out of trouble. Right? Wrong. I know because of what happened when I went on this honesty kick last fall. In the first place, I almost lost my best friend. And then I practically spoiled Christmas for our entire family.

What had set me off on this truth business

1

was the lies I found all around me, including my own. I began counting once and gave up. I decided you'd need a computer to keep track of them. They're all around, like germs.

Even signs lie. For instance, we live in a place called *Squires' Park Estates*. It isn't a park and there are no estates. Just plain houses, not big either — built around a little pond that once belonged to a man named Squires. Each house is on a ninety-foot lot. You can't call that an *estate*. They've planted some trees around the pond — willows that are still skinny and skimpy. It's nice, but it's not a *park*. But that's what the sign at the entrance says: SQUIRES' PARK ESTATES. Even my parents find it embarrassing. My mother laughs when she's giving people directions to get here. "A slight exaggeration," she says, speaking of the sign.

I don't think Mother realizes that she isn't exactly truthful herself. She's a fine person in every way, but she does tell a lie at least once a week. Especially on the phone. She'll tell the person she's talking to that something is burning, or that somebody's at the door. The truth is, she doesn't want to talk to that person any longer and is too chicken to say so.

Another example: The other day Mother met Aunt Irma at the library and said, "You look wonderful." Aunt Irma had had an operation. That night at dinner Mother said to Daddy, "Irma looks terrible. I'm worried." Mother doesn't call this lying. She calls it being tactful.

Daddy is basically honest. In fact, he once told me it was important to tell the truth because otherwise no one would trust you. But even Daddy fibs once in a while. On Saturday or Sunday mornings the phone will wake him out of a dead sleep and I'll hear him say, "No, no. That's all right. We were up." I asked him about it once, and he said he wanted to spare his friend's feelings. "Ed would feel terrible if he thought he woke me up." But I think the real reason Daddy lied was that he was ashamed to be sleeping so late.

And then there's my little brother Peter, who tells the wildest stories you ever heard. He told the Overtons that Daddy was getting a motorcycle to ride to the train station. The Overtons are old and don't like noise, and they called up Daddy to protest. Then Peter told the Fletchers who live next door that Daddy was going to live in Florida.

"He's going to fly there in a plane," Peter said. "And I'm going with him. We're going to live there, him and me. Mommy and the girls are going to stay here."

So Mrs. Fletcher told some other neighbors

that our parents must be getting a divorce. Mother heard about it and explained that Peter has "an overactive imagination." She doesn't call what he does lying, either, and I guess he is too little to know the difference. He's only six.

My sister Sherry, on the other hand, is certainly old enough to know better. She's sixteen. And she's the worst fibber in the family, if not in the known world.

On Tuesday, somebody named Howard called up and asked her to go to the movies. She said she had a toothache. That was a real put-on. We all have good teeth. We get them from the Mitchells, Mother says. She was a Mitchell before she married Daddy. Sherry has never had a toothache in her life.

On Thursday a boy named Mark called to ask her to go to a football game, and she said she was swamped with homework. And when Warren asked her, she said we were going to Grandma's that weekend. "I'm sorry," she said.

"That's two lies," I told her when she had hung up. "We're not going to Grandma's; she's coming here, and you know it. And you're not sorry. You're just hoping *Tommy* will ask you."

"It's none of your business," Sherry

snapped. "Besides, those are just white lies. I may not want to go to the game with Mark or Warren, but I want to keep them as friends. You keep on the way you did with Alison and you won't have a friend in the world."

"I was only telling the truth," I insisted.

It was odd that telling the truth should have caused the trouble with Alison, who had been my best friend up to then, because it was a lie that brought us together.

Chapter 2

ALISON MORSE MOVED to Squires' Park last summer, just before school started. I first met her at the bus stop. The minute I saw her I thought we ought to be friends.

I figured she must be my age. (It turned out she is exactly two months older.) She was about my size and had on the same kind of skirt I was wearing that day. The main difference was our hair. Mine is a mousey tan and hardly reaches my shoulders. Alison's was long and dark and beautiful.

I didn't get much chance to talk to her before the bus came. "Hi!" I said, and told her my name.

"Kimberly?" she said. "That's pretty."

I explained that Mother thinks if you have Jones for a last name, you have to have a fancy first name or you'll be lost in the crowd.

"For instance," I said. "I have an older sister and her name is Sheridan. Only we call her Sherry, of course. Have you any sisters or brothers?"

"Just a sister — Lila. She's four years older than I am, and my parents think she's perfect."

I gave her a sympathetic nod. That was something else we had in common — older sisters who were a pain.

"I'd rather have had a brother," Alison said. "Or a sister nearer my own age. Then I would have someone to do things with. Like days when you have to stay near home. Know what I mean?"

I nodded again. She was going to have someone now, I was thinking — me. The Morses' house was only a five-minute walk from ours, at the north end of the pond. I'd made quite a few friends since we had moved here from Hartsdale three years ago, but I didn't have one special friend the way my brother Peter did.

Peter met Kenny Walker the day we moved in, and they've played together practically every day since. Kenny is a year older, and Peter learns a lot from him. Kenny has two older brothers, twelve and thirteen. What he learns from them, Kenny passes on to Peter in the form of a one-way quiz.

"Know how many parts in a propellor? Two hundred. Know what an altimefer is? A barometer that tells how far off the ground a plane is." Things like that. So at six, Peter's head is crammed with a lot of random information — all of it correct, incidentally. But Peter still seems adorable and sweet to us. I guess it's because he's the baby of the family.

I pointed Peter out to Alison. "That's my brother over there — the little blonde one. He's real cute. I'm not just saying so because he's my brother — he really is." He was with the Walker boys, Kenny and Glenn and Martin.

Alison looked at them with considerable interest. The Walker boys are very good-looking. Glenn is tall, and Martin has this terrific smile.

"Have you got a boy friend?" Alison asked in

an offhand way, picking a wild aster growing at our feet.

I have a special answer for embarrassing questions. It's this: "Why do you ask?" It always works. It puts the other person on the spot. They've got to admit they're being nosey, or back down. Usually they wiggle out of it by saying, "Oh, I was just wondering." Then, unless they're terribly curious, they'll drop it. But by now I was curious myself. "Not right now," I said, which was a cop-out. I'd never had one. "Why? Do you?"

Alison wrinkled her nose. "I hate boys."

I knew what she really meant was that she didn't have a boy friend, either. Still another thing we had in common. "Me, too," I said.

We got to school, and it turned out we were in the same homeroom. We were starting the sixth grade and went to a different room for each subject. And this year our subjects had new names. Social Studies was Social Sciences. Our first class was Language Arts. Alison and I were the first ones to figure out that that meant English, so we got there first. The teacher wasn't even there yet.

Some of the kids had gone to the art room. Others had gone to the French or Spanish rooms in the Junior High building. So we had our choice of seats.

"Where do you want to sit?" Alison asked. It was understood that we would sit next to each other whenever we could.

"The middle rows are the best," I told her. "Teachers always expect the kids in back to be bad, so they keep watching the back rows. And naturally they see everything up front. Here. What about these two?"

Alison nodded absently. She was holding something. "Look."

It was a little gold-colored pin in the shape of a dachshund. "That's darling," I said. "I love dachshunds."

She handed it to me. "You can have it, then."

"Why? Don't you want it anymore?"

"I found it on the desk. And I have one like it at home. Only the pin part is broken. And mine has a red eye."

This one had a tiny green stone eye, just like an emerald. It was the cutest pin I'd ever seen. I could wear it with my good green dress. Just then the teacher came in — Mr. Barber.

"Good morning, girls. Where is everyone else?" His face was as wrinkled as a tobacco leaf, but he had a kind look.

"I think I hear them coming now," I said. Then I lowered my voice. "Do you think I can keep it?"

12

"Why not?" Alison said. "Finders keepers."

I certainly wanted to keep it. I love dogs, but dachshunds are my favorites. We can't keep a dog because my mother is allergic to fur. She has asthma and has to use an inhaler sometimes. But when I grow up and live alone in a penthouse and earn money, the first thing I'm going to buy is a miniature dachshund. I saw one in the pet shop and nearly died. It looked like a toy. And the man said it would never get any bigger. I can hardly wait. The little pin would be a reminder of the real dog I would have someday.

"Thanks, Alison," I whispered and dropped the pin in my pocket. The rest of the kids had come in.

Alison and I smiled in a secret way and sat down. As Mr. Barber greeted the class and made his opening speech, I thought how lucky it was that Alison had moved to Squires' Park. None of the other girls in the class lived that close. If I wanted to play with them, their mothers had to drive them over, and they didn't always want to. My mother works at the reception desk at the hospital so she can't drive me anywhere except on her day off or on weekends.

I was sure Alison and I would have a lot in

common. She could have her pin fixed, and we could wear them together. We could have a secret club, and they could be our club pins. We could call ourselves The Dachs — for dachshunds. And if her pin couldn't be fixed, we could wear them on chains around our necks.

I hadn't been listening to Mr. Barber, but suddenly he stopped talking. A girl from another class had come in and was standing by his desk. She must have been new. I had never seen her before. She spoke quietly to Mr. Barber, who listened and then turned to the class.

"Has anyone found a pin?" he asked. I guess this was the girl's homeroom. She had probably dropped it. "A little pin in the shape of a dog?"

"No, Mr. Barber," the class chorused.

I didn't know what to do. The pin was in my pocket. If it hadn't been for that, I would have given it to her. I hadn't thought about it belonging to somebody. Only that it was cute and that it had been nice of Alison to give it to me. I couldn't take it out of my pocket in front of the whole class. They'd all know that I had meant to keep it.

Mr. Barber and the girl looked around the

room, waiting. I glanced at Alison. She was the one who had found the pin. Her cheeks were a deep pink, and she sat looking straight ahead. Of course Alison couldn't say she had found it, I realized. She would have to tell what she'd done with it and that would make me look like a thief. My cheeks felt as hot as Alison's looked.

I knew that I should have given the pin to Mr. Barber at the beginning of the class. It was too late now. So much time had gone by that I couldn't speak up. Everyone would wonder why I hadn't admitted right away that I had the pin. "He who hesitates is lost," flashed through my mind. I felt lost, all right.

"A little pin in the shape of a dog?" Mr. Barber asked again.

"No, Mr. Barber." Alison and I were silent and our faces grew redder. Thank goodness we're in the middle, I thought.

"I guess not. I'm sorry," Mr. Barber said, and the girl left.

The lesson went on but I didn't hear a word. I kept thinking of the pin in my pocket and feeling awful. What if there was a hole in my pocket and Mr. Barber sent me to the blackboard and the pin fell out! I pinned it inside, to make sure. If only I'd just put it on my desk! I thought. And I heard myself saying innocently, "Is this it? I just noticed it." Or, why hadn't I bent over and pretended to find it on the floor: "Look! It was there all the time."

I didn't dare look at anybody for fear they'd tell by my eyes that I had stolen goods in my pocket. I scribbled and doodled all over my assignment book. Luckily, Mr. Barber didn't call on me. And after what seemed like several years, class was over.

I waited for Alison in the hall.

"What are we going to do?" she whispered. "If you wear it, everyone will know. Should we just chuck it out?"

Her saying "we" showed me she felt as responsible as I did. I thought a minute. "I know. I'll take it to Lost and Found."

"*Can* you?"

Sure. But I'll have to wait till classes are over. Save a place for me on the bus."

I was a little nervous about handing in the pin, but there was nothing to it. "I found this in the hall," I said, my fingers crossed behind my back. "Somebody must have dropped it."

"Thank you." The woman in the office didn't even look at me.

"Now I know how jewel thieves feel when they've got a hot diamond," I said to Alison, on the bus.

"So do I." She slid over on the seat. "But at least we got rid of it. I mean, you did."

It had been rough, but it united us in a special way, like people who have been shipwrecked together, or in a prison camp. I walked with Alison as far as her house, and then went on with Peter and Kenny.

"Know what a tachometer is for on a sports car?" Kenny was asking. "It tells how fast the motor — not the car — is going. Know what M.G. really means? Morris Garage. Know what T.A.S.C. stands for? Taconic Auto Sports Club." Their usual conversation.

As soon as I got home I telephoned Alison to remind her not to say anything about the pin at home.

"Don't worry. I wouldn't."

So that was okay. Never again, I vowed. That's the worst kind of lie, I thought. The sneaky, silent kind. Never again. And yet — just a few weeks later, I was in trouble again, for a very stupid, very ordinary kind of lie. It was the kind of lie all kids tell. Only in my case it was, as usual, bigger and better.

Chapter 3

EVERYBODY FAKES BOOK reports. That's nothing new. I didn't only fake mine, I made it up out of about fifty lies.

It's a wonder to me that teachers go on assigning outside reading. At least half the kids get their reports from other kids or make them up from the stuff on the book jacket. If *I'm* smart enough to know that, you'd think teachers would be. They've been to college. But I guess they're incurable optimists. They go on hoping they'll have a class of kids who will really read books and give honest reports on them. Mr. Barber loves books so much himself, I guess it never occurs to him that anybody would ever skip reading one.

I like books myself. I'd rather read six books than do one math assignment. And I like Mr. Barber. I never would have faked anything in his class if I hadn't been in a jam. What happened was that the day after Halloween, all the paper pumpkins and skeletons and everything disappeared from the stores and, like magic, there were Christmas trees and cards and decorations and toys. Peter saw them and started talking about what he wanted Santa to bring him.

Mother blew her top. Not at Peter, but at "Them."

"They start earlier every year," she said. "It's disgusting." At dinner she said to Daddy, "Can you imagine! This early! It's not even Thanksgiving and they're showing Christmas things!" They both did some talking about how Christmas was spoiled by commercialism, and Mother decreed that we would not be influenced by it. We were going to have an old-fashioned Christmas and make all our gifts.

That was fine with me. I never have much money and I love making things. I called Alison and told her my plans as soon as I had figured what I would make. A macramé belt for my mother. A tie for Daddy. A Snoopy dog wall plaque for Peter.

"Kim," she said. "You always have so many ideas. What can I give Lila?"

I couldn't answer that. I hadn't yet figured what I would make for Sherry. She was a problem. But I was sure to think of something. I told Alison I'd call her as soon as I had an idea. I didn't mind her copying at all. In fact, we could work on them together. So I kept looking through magazines, trying to find something that would be pretty, useful, inexpensive, and easy to make. Naturally it kept me busy. I kept putting off my reading assignment.

All of a sudden, it was the day to hand in our reports, and I hadn't even taken a book from the library.

"Kimberly?" Mr. Barber asked. "You have your report?"

I had once told Mr. Barber how much I loved reading. He was looking at me so expectantly that I didn't have the heart to tell him I hadn't even chosen a book.

"Yes, Mr. Barber. But I left it home. I forgot today was the day." That part was true, anyway.

"Bring it in tomorrow."

"Yes, Mr. Barber."

Everybody had already taken out all the good books from the school library. Our public library is open evenings, so I got Mother to take me there. But in the library I got to looking at books on handicrafts and checked them out instead. My mind was so full of ceramics and tie-dye scarves and other things, I forgot to take out another book.

The next day when Mr. Barber asked for my report, I had to tell another lie. "Oh, I forgot! I had it right by my books, too!" I said. "I'll bring it tomorrow."

But Mother and Daddy were going out, and I couldn't get to the library that night. So the next day I told Mr. Barber I had lost my report.

"Lost it, Kimberly?" Mr. Barber said doubtfully. "Wasn't that unusually careless of you?"

"Well, I didn't exactly lose it. It was on my desk with some other papers. Some were rumply, where I'd done my math over. And I guess it got thrown out. We have a new maid. I guess she did it. I know she threw out some of Daddy's papers, and he was furious. He said,

'Elke, don't ever touch my papers.' She's Swedish. She said, 'Yah, Mr. Jones.' "

We have never had a maid. I don't know what gets into me. Sometimes when I start fibbing I get carried away. I probably would have gone on to imitate Elke's conversation further if Mr. Barber hadn't stopped me.

"That's enough, Kimberly." He passed a hand over his brown, wrinkled forehead. "You still have the book, I suppose. You haven't lost that?"

"What? Oh, the book. No, of course not."

"Good. Suppose you give me the title, for my records. And I will allow you one more day to turn in your report."

"The title?" My mind was a blank. I couldn't even think of the title of the last book I'd read. I looked around as if hoping to find one written on the air. On my right was nothing but windows. On my left, the blackboard all washed clean. On the front wall there was a picture of a lady in a field of brownish grass. She was looking up at a house on a hill.

"*The House on the Hill*," I said.

Mr. Barber wrote it down. "*The House on the Hill*, by...?"

"Pardon me?"

"The name of the author, if you please."

"Oh," I stalled, "you mean the person who wrote the book."

"Yes, that is what we call a person who writes a book," he said. Not sarcastically, though. Just as if he were tired.

Roberta Lawson, sitting in the front row, snickered and looked at William Reeves. They both get A's in everything. Two creeps.

"*The House on the Hill*, by Robert Williams." I said, putting their names together. "Robert L.R. Williams." Two middle initials made the name different enough to be convincing, I thought.

Mr. Barber wrote that down, too. "An author I've never heard of," he said, as if confessing an oversight. "We'll see your report tomorrow, then. No, on second thought, in view of your tendency to lose things, you had better come to this room at three o'clock and write it here."

"Stay after school!" I cried. "What about my little brother? I'm supposed to see that he gets home from the bus."

"If your brother is old enough to be in this school, he's old enough to get home. You can take the second bus." The subject was closed.

At three o'clock I sat in his classroom and tried to think. Mr. Barber went over papers on his desk. The other desks were empty. The clock ticked noisily and the minute hand jumped. Mr. Barber had given me an outline to fill out. Six questions. In ten minutes I had filled out only the first two: 1. Title of book. 2. Author. The third question was, What is the book about? (Sum up the story in your own words.)

It would be my own words, all right. How could I sum up a story that didn't exist? I looked at the picture on the wall. Mr. Barber had told us that it was a print of a famous painting in a New York museum. The name of the picture was "Christina's World." That title just didn't make sense to me. The lady in the grass had straggly hair and funny, knobby arms. She looked as if she had fallen down. As if maybe she'd been running after somebody and had tripped or just got tired. And the way she was looking up at the house made me think the person she was trying to catch was hiding there.

The house was sort of old and deserted-looking to me. I narrowed my eyes and tried to see something move. I can do that sometimes. An eye in a portrait will blink. I stared through half-closed lids, and a curtain in the old house flickered. Somebody was hiding there, all right. Who was it? I started writing.

"3. This story is about a girl who ran away from home. Her parents were dead, and she was being raised by a mean governess. The governess wouldn't give her more than ten cents a week even though her parents had left her a lot of money."

The girl had to have a name. After thinking a long while I named her Eugenia Farrow. Farrow after my first-grade teacher who was the nicest teacher in the world, and Eugenia because it sounded like someone in a book — different and romantic.

The governess had to have a name too. Miss Meany? No, what about Miss Strict? Strictman? Miss Strictland. That was good.

I wrote on. "After her parents died Eugenia had a terrible time. It was nothing but rules, rules, rules, so one day she ran away. Miss Strictland, her mean governess, noticed right away that she was gone and came after her. Eugenia ran as fast as she could, but although Miss Strictland was old, she was a good runner. Eugenia could hear her coming behind her wherever she turned.

"At last Eugenia got an idea. There was an old house on the hill that nobody ever went near. Everybody thought it was haunted. But Eugenia didn't believe it. Anyway, she was brave. She climbed in through an open window. She knew her mean governess wouldn't dare follow her there. Sure enough, Miss Strickland fell down in the grass and didn't go any further."

A bell rang. It was time for the second bus already.

"Not finished yet?" Mr. Barber asked.

"Just the first three questions."

He took what I had done and told me to finish the rest at home. "You certainly wrote a lot," he commented. "A paragraph would have been enough."

I had written nearly a page and a half. It wasn't really a summary, either. But I couldn't help that.

I started working on the other questions as soon as I got home. They were: 4. What was your favorite part? 5. Which were your favorite characters? and 6. Did you like it? If so, why?

The last one would be easy. But before I could answer the others, I had to do some more thinking. I didn't get to watch television that night. I didn't even get to do my other homework assignments. It took me until bedtime to finish my report.

I finally wrote: "4. My favorite part was

where Eugenia finds this little room off the attic in the house. In the room lives a little old woman who looks like a witch but isn't, her grandson, and his pet monkey. 5. My favorite characters were Eugenia, with her beautiful long dark hair, and the boy with the monkey. 6. Yes, I liked this book very much because it was interesting and exciting." Whew! It was finished at last.

The next day on the bus I told Alison what I had done. She looked at me as if I were a genius. "Kim, you're terrific!"

"Terrifically dumb, you mean. I had to work ten times as hard as if I'd just read a book and reported on it. And after all my work old Barber Pole will probably find out and give me a zero."

He didn't, though. As a matter of fact, he wrote VERY GOOD on my paper. But I'll never try *that* again!

Now, it would certainly seem that with that experience coming on top of the one about the pin, I would have stopped fibbing. But I didn't.

Chapter 4

BECAUSE OF SPENDING all that time on Language Arts, I hadn't done the homework for my other subjects. In Social Sciences, the class had started studying the French Revolution. I hadn't read the assignment. I was hoping to skim through it while the others were reciting. Just my luck, Miss Hodges called on me first.

"You've read Chapter Thirteen, Kimberly?"

"Yes, mostly, Miss Hodges."

"Good. Will you tell us what a tumbril is?"

"A tumbril?"

"Yes." Miss Hodges wrote the word on the blackboard.

"It's a kind of drinking glass. Sort of a goblet."

Somebody in the back row said, "Haw haw!" And then the rest of the boys started laughing. Miss Hodges drew a picture on the blackboard. I think she's a frustrated artist. She was drawing a picture of a little wagon, for some reason.

In the front row Roberta Lawson was throwing her hand up so wildly that I almost expected it to fall off and land in the aisle.

Miss Hodges looked up. "Yes, Roberta?"

"A tumbril is a cart they used during the French Revolution to carry people to the guillotine." Roberta sat down looking smug. She is never late with her homework. The minute she spoke I realized I had confused the word with "tumbler." The kids in the back were still laughing.

"How about a nice tumbril of lemonade?" one of them asked. The others fell out of their seats laughing. I felt smaller than a baby ant and wished I was one so I could crawl away into a crack in the floor. I couldn't concentrate during the rest of the class.

Of all the trouble I'd had that term, that was the thing that made me feel worst. Feeling guilty because you almost kept something belonging to somebody else is bad. Having to do a lot of extra work because you've fibbed is bad, too. But nothing is as bad as being laughed at. And knowing that you deserved it.

I even felt embarrassed with Alison. Going home on the bus, she carefully chattered about other things, but I knew I'd been an idiot. Such a dumb answer! And just like me — pretending. Nobody would have laughed if I'd said, "I don't know." I spent the afternoon catching up on my homework. That night at dinner when I saw our glasses — tall ones with stems for all but Peter — I remembered how stupid I'd been. I had no sooner picked up my milk when I put it down, untouched.

"How about a tumbril of lemonade?" I heard in my head, and gave a shudder.

"Have you caught cold, Kim?" Mother asked. "Would you like an aspirin?"

We have this mild aspirin for kids that tastes like orange candy. "*I have a cold*," Peter said, and gave such an artificial sneeze we all laughed. Peter laughed himself. He's got a great disposition. So I felt okay again. But afterward, up in my room I made an oath. I wrote

31

it out on paper. *I will never lie again. Signed, Kimberly Jones.* I pricked my thumb with a needle and smeared blood on the paper. Then I put it in an envelope, sealed it and wrote on the outside, *Pledge. Not to be broken.*

I kept my pledge, too, although it was hard at times. All through November, which is a gloomy month anyway, I stuck to it. After a while I got into the swing of it, and it seemed natural. People sometimes looked at me in surprise when I'd tell them truthfully what I thought about something. And Mother would apologize.

"I'm afraid Kim is dreadfully outspoken these days," she would say. "It's a phase she's going through."

I was simply being honest. The way people are supposed to be. And what happened? I got in worse trouble than I ever had telling fibs. Much worse.

The Saturday after Thanksgiving — a gray, chilly day — I called Alison. "Come on over. I've got an idea for a present for Sherry. I've got all the stuff to make it, and there's enough for you. You can make one for Lila."

I had decided to make a fancy cover for Sherry's hair spray can. I had some colored felt, some glue and spangles. Everything was in a pillowcase so Sherry wouldn't see it if she walked in.

"I can't come now," Alison said. "I'm going to get my hair done."

"Well, tell your mother to be quick and come over for lunch. We can have our special sandwiches."

I had invented having cream cheese and chopped nuts on sour rye with seeds. Mother says that's crazy, that you should have ham on rye, and you should have cream cheese and nuts on raisin bread. But Alison and I like it our way.

"I can't come to lunch," Alison said. "We're having it out. Mom is taking me to her hairdresser."

"Yuck! What are they going to do to you?"

"Mom calls it 'styling.' Trim my hair and wash it, I guess. I'll come over as soon as we get back."

Good! I thought. My hair was taking ages to grow. Hair takes longer in the winter, Mother says. It was a help that Alison was getting hers trimmed a little. We were alike in so many ways. We liked the same people and the same things. We liked Mr. Barber and hated the math teacher. We had two outfits alike already. Maybe we could get more. I looked at myself in the hall mirror. My hair was almost to my shoulders. With Alison getting hers trimmed, we'd look even more alike. If only it was the same color, I thought, people might take us for sisters. We'd tell them we were! *"We're both adopted. But don't ever, ever mention it. Our parents are terribly sensitive about it. They would just deny it."*

I could hardly wait for Alison to come. We could have such fun deciding who our real parents would be. If only her hair were lighter or mine darker! Suddenly I had an idea. Everybody was too busy to pay any attention — that was good. Daddy was out getting a few bulbs planted before the ground froze hard. Mother had set up the sewing machine in the kitchen. She was making a quilted robe for Sherry for Christmas. Sherry was downtown shopping. Peter was playing with Kenny in his own room, flying little planes around.

"Know how fast birds can fly?" Kenny was asking. "Little birds can fly about thirty miles an hour. Crows and ducks can go forty. Some birds can even go sixty. Martin and Glenn looked it up." They were too busy to snoop on me.

Perfect, I thought, and looked for Mother's hair coloring stuff. Mother calls it a "rinse."

"It's just to cover the premature gray at my temples," she says, as if she wasn't mature.

I found the stuff on the top shelf of the linen closet where Mother keeps bath oil and shampoo and stuff. It was called SO-SOFT E*Z TINT. I took it into the bathroom and locked the door. After I'd taken off my T-shirt I read the directions. "Your So-Soft Tint is easy to use. Just add bottle A to bottle B. Shake gently and apply, starting at center part. Rub well and proceed until entire head is covered. Be sure to wear rubber gloves and wipe any color off skin immediately."

I had forgotten rubber gloves. I slipped out, found the gloves on the bottom shelf of the same closet and came back. I dumped some tint on my center part and started to rub. It didn't sting or anything. This is fun, I was thinking. Maybe Alison and I could open a beauty parlor for kids and make money for Christmas presents. It didn't say how long you were supposed to rub. I picked up the bottle to read the directions. Just then the door opened. I had forgotten to lock it again.

"Kimberly! What on earth are you doing!" Mother said.

I jumped, and the bottle slipped out of my hand. A dark stain began to spread over the rug and the floor. Darn! I thought, why didn't I think of this yesterday when Mother was at work? Mother began to yell. I grabbed a towel and started wiping the floor.

"Not with that!" Mother shouted. "That's a good guest towel!"

She got some rags and then some spray cleaner and bleach. Most of the stain came off the floor, but you can still see a dark place if you move the new rug which we had to buy. And my neck and ears stayed brown for days. I didn't get to wipe the color off until we were through with the floor. It didn't come out of my hair, either, though Mother shampooed it twice. I begged her to put a few streaks here and there so it would look as if it were meant to be that way. Some of Mother's friends have striped hair and it looks pretty. But she wouldn't do it.

Daddy came in for lunch. His ears were red. "I hope you've got something hot for lunch. It's cold out."

"How can I make a hot lunch when I've got Kimberly to contend with?" Mother cried, and told him what I'd done.

"That must be a strong dye," Daddy said.

"If it's a dye," I demanded, "why don't they say so on the bottle? Why do they call it a 'tint'?"

Everybody was standing around by then. Sherry had come back with her packages. Peter and Kenny were having sandwiches. Mother's sewing was put away.

"And Mother calls it a rinse," I went on. "If it's a rinse it ought to rinse out."

"Women don't like the word 'dye,'" Sherry said. "They prefer to use a euphemism."

"Is *that* what you used?" Peter asked me, his eyes wide.

We all laughed. But I didn't know what the word meant, either. And after the way I'd been caught on "tumbril" I wasn't going to pretend. "What's a euphemism?"

Daddy said it was the use of a more polite word instead of a franker one that might not be as acceptable.

I understood. "I see. Like saying you have to go to the powder room, or the ladies room."

"When you have to...," Peter began.

Mother interrupted. "Be quiet and drink your milk, Peter." But he and Kenny whispered to each other and giggled.

Thinking it over, I decided that Mother and her friends talk in euphemisms all the time. It's practically their entire conversation. And it wasn't exactly honest — saying one thing when you mean another. But it gave me an idea.

Alison and I would make up a private language. Then we'd be able to talk to each other, and nobody would know what we were saying. We could say awful things about Mr. Fenshaw, the coach, right in front of him. And tell Mrs. Gettleson, the math teacher, right to her face that she was a rat. And she'd never know it. I couldn't wait for Alison to come.

When the doorbell finally rang, I got a shock. I just stood there staring. Alison's hair was cut short...there was hardly any of it left. Alison was staring at me, too. But I had forgotten about my own hair.

"What happened?" I asked.

"I told them I only wanted it a little shorter, but they gave me a Pixie."

Her hair was much shorter than Peter's. It didn't even cover her ears. I kept staring and shaking my head.

"Close the door," Mother called. "You're making the house cold." But I didn't move.

Alison was surprisingly cheerful. "My head feels so light, I can't get used to it. Mommy says it will be a lot easier to take care of this way. No snarls. What happened to *your* hair?"

I didn't bother to answer. It didn't matter now whether my hair was brown or blonde or half of each, which it was. I felt terrible. I had

liked Alison so much just the way she was, and now she had changed. To think that all her beautiful hair was gone! She had sometimes worn it in two braids, sometimes just hanging loose, sometimes in a pony-tail. She looked pretty all those ways. Now she looked awful. Her face looked too big and her ears stuck out.

"What do you think?" she asked, showing me the back.

I never considered telling her anything but the truth. "It's awful. It makes you look ugly."

Chapter 5

ALISON'S MOUTH FELL open. Her eyes grew wide and shiny. Mother had come to close the door.

"Kimberly! What a thing to say! Alison looks very...*chic.* You do, Alison, that short hair gives you a real...*gamine* look."

That's another way Mother gets around telling the truth. She throws in a foreign word nobody can understand. "You wait and see, Kim," she said. "In a few days you'll be wanting yours cut short like that."

I shuddered. "Never!"

Alison tossed her head. (She would have tossed her hair but now there wasn't enough.) "All right for you, Kimberly Jones! I'm never going to speak to you again!" She walked away fast.

Mother looked as if she wanted to shake me. "Kimberly! How could you! Your best friend! Don't you see how hurt she was?"

"Why blame me? I didn't do it. Go talk to the guy at the beauty shop, Mister John, or whatever his name is. He's the one who cut it."

Mother went on as if she hadn't heard me.

"That poor child! I don't blame her for saying she didn't want to speak to you again. It's just what you deserve."

I thought Alison would come to her senses. All she had to do was look in the mirror and she'd see I was right. What was she mad at me for? I was the one who should be mad. Look at all the trouble I'd gone to trying to make my hair dark. I figured she'd cool off and give me a call.

But when the phone rang it was Mrs. Morse. Mother talked to her. She said about a million times that she was sorry, and that she didn't know what had gotten into me lately, I'd been talking like that to everybody. After a while they got talking about how difficult it was to raise children in these permissive times, and got off my back. Pretty soon they were making a date to meet and go shopping on Mother's next day off.

Then I heard Mother say, "Put Alison on. Let's see if we can't patch things up. Come here, Kim. Alison wants to talk to you," Mother called.

When I ran in, Mother took a tight hold of my arm. "You apologize!" she hissed.

On the other end of the phone I could hear Mrs. Morse whispering to Alison. "I insist," she was saying. "At least listen to what Kim has to say."

I didn't see why I should apologize. I hadn't done anything wrong. All I had done was tell the truth. Isn't that what friends are supposed to do? Alison didn't say anything. Not even hello. I could just hear her breathing. Sniffing, sort of.

I pictured her standing there with her ears sticking out and her eyes red. How could I say that she didn't look ugly? That I hadn't meant it? I kept thinking of all that nice hair on the beauty parlor floor. If Alison didn't want it herself, I thought, I'd be glad to have it.

"Listen, Alison," I said. "I have an idea. Why don't we call the beauty shop and tell them to save the hair. They can make you a wig."

Alison yowled. Mother grabbed the phone from me and gave my bottom a slap. "That's enough, young lady. Haven't you done enough harm?" Everybody thought I meant it as a crack. And Mother went through her apology routine again.

"I was only telling the truth," I kept saying.

It went on and on and on, right through dinner. We were having turkey pie. I was tired of leftover turkey, but the crust was good.

"Don't you want me to be honest?" I asked when they kept yammering at me.

"Not if it means hurting someone, no," Mother said. "Being honest is one thing; being brutally frank is another."

Sherry was carefully picking pieces of turkey out of the cream sauce and eating them, leaving little squares of potato and the crust. She's on a diet again.

"Kim has no idea of how to be tactful," she said.

"How to lie, you mean. I want to tell the truth, like George Washington," I said.

I looked at Daddy. I expected him to take my side, especially after what he'd said about people not trusting you if you didn't tell the truth.

"That story about Washington and the cherry tree is a myth, I'm afraid, Kim," he said. "It was invented by a Parson Weems. And somehow, it caught on, as stories do. It was promoted further in the public mind when someone made a painting of the scene."

"Parson Weems!" I put down my fork. "*Parson* Weems, and it was just a put-on?" I'd heard that story since I was little. To think it was a lie! And that a parson had told it! I shook my head in amazement. Everybody was deceitful. I stuck my fork in a hole in the table cloth and twisted it absently. Everybody tells lies, I was thinking, even clergymen.

"Don't do that, Kim," Mother said. "You're making that hole bigger. I'm the one who has to mend it. I should think by this time you'd be old enough to show a little consideration for others. Aren't you ever going to grow up?"

"I hope not," I said in what I hoped was a cutting tone. "I hope I don't. If being grown-up means being a phony, I'd rather be retarded."

"I'm not sure you're not," said Sherry.

I glared at Sherry.

"Now, Sherry," Mother reproved.

"I don't see why Alison was so upset," I muttered. "I didn't say anything so terrible."

Sherry looked across the table as if she hadn't seen me before. "What's Kimberly done to her hair? Why has she got that brown stripe down the middle?" As if she'd forgotten.

"It's nice, like a chipmunk," Peter said.

"I hope you're not going to let her go *out* looking like that," Sherry said. "She looks repulsive."

"I do not!" I slid down in my chair, reaching out with my foot, trying to kick her under the table. "I do not!"

Sherry gave a cool smile. "See how it feels? Do you still wonder why Alison was upset? She, at least, looks normal. You look like something escaped from the zoo."

"Like a chipmunk," Peter agreed.

"Now, Sherry," Mother said again, taking my side for once. "You tried to bleach your hair, remember. All girls experiment. I know I did. When I was at boarding school, we did all sorts of crazy things, my roommate and I. We went on fad diets and tried to make our hair red, and one time Margo and I let our nails grow long and then clipped a 'v' out of the middle of each nail, so it had two sharp points."

"I'm glad I didn't know you then," Daddy

said. "Imagine what you could do if you were mad at someone. Tear them to pieces."

"We almost scratched *ourselves* to pieces." Mother looked at her nails. She keeps them in nice ovals with pink polish. "I wonder where Margo is now. She was my best friend at the time."

It might be fun to try, I thought. Alison and I could let our nails grow and cut them in points like that with Daddy's nail clippers. We could have a club and call ourselves "The Tigers."

Only—Alison wasn't going to speak to me again.

Chapter 6

THE POND AT Squires' Park froze, and I went skating. Alison was skating, too, but when she saw me she skated away. At school she never looked in my direction. She sat with Patty Jo Busch on the bus and played with her after school. Patty Jo lives at Squires' Park, too, but she's nearly two years younger than we are.

I had no one to play with. I was bored. But all

the time I kept telling myself, "I don't care. I'm *not* going to break my pledge. There are too many phonies in the world."

Christmas vacation came, and the weather was awful. It rained for two days. Then some snowy slush fell and spoiled the ice. The big boys shoveled a rink and left the slush in big piles around it. The little kids ran around the rest of the slush, and that night their footprints froze and the pond had bumps all over. So there was no more skating. Daddy said we needed a good thaw and then another freeze.

Not being able to skate made things worse. I missed Alison. Luckily, I had all those Christmas presents to make, and that kept me busy. I had to help Peter make presents, too. He watched me working, and I gave him scraps of material. His method was to make something first and *then* decide what it was. He rolled up a small scrap of red felt, glued it together and after looking at it awhile, decided it was a thimble holder. Then he hinged two pieces of cardboard at one edge with scotch tape and said it was for Daddy — "a paper to hold papers."

So during all the bad weather, there I was, playing with a six-year-old. But I didn't really mind. Peter is so cute and funny. And I hadn't told a lie for nearly two months. I had kept my record straight.

And then, just a week before Christmas, my pledge was put to a real test. I was faced with a question I *couldn't* answer truthfully. It was a real dilemma.

The weather had behaved as if taking orders from Daddy. There was a thaw — all the lumps and footsteps on the pond melted, and then the weather turned cold. But it was a nice kind of cold with the nicest kind of snow. Big flakes came swirling past the windows like falling petals. We had hamburgers and frozen French fries for dinner because Mother and Daddy were going out. Sherry had a part in the school play, and naturally they wanted to see it. Mother left her dessert on the table and went back to the telephone. She'd been calling around all afternoon and hadn't been able to get a baby sitter. When she came back to the table for her coffee, Mother was about to give up. All the girls who usually baby-sat for people were either in the play, or working backstage on props or prompting or were acting as ushers.

"You've got to see it," I said. "Sherry is really great." Sherry had the second most important part. I had seen the play myself that afternoon. Grades five to nine always get to see the dress rehearsals. "I can take care of Peter," I said.

Mother looked doubtful.

"I've been taking care of him all afternoon," I pointed out. "What's the difference?"

"I think Kim can manage," Daddy said. "She's a sensible girl."

"Oh, I don't know," Mother said. "I don't like to leave them alone at night."

I exploded. "You let Sherry baby-sit, for other people even, when *she* was eleven."

"Sherry," Mother said, "has always been very mature for her age."

I made a noise. "I wish those Planned Parenthood people would take some action," I said. "They ought to get Congress to pass a law that couples could only have one child. Then your parents wouldn't be comparing you with somebody."

But of course, I realized, if they passed that law I wouldn't have a little brother. Come to think of it, I wouldn't be here, either. But it would be nice to be judged for myself for a change.

"Maybe I could get somebody to come and baby-sit with me." I was thinking of Alison, of course. She'd never get a chance to baby-sit going around with Patty Jo, because Patty Jo wouldn't be old enough to be a sitter for years.

"Oh, for heaven's sake, Mother!" Sherry said. "Let Kim do it. She's not a baby, and it isn't as if we lived in the wilderness. There's a house every few feet. In fact, we're surrounded with neighbors."

"That's so," Mother admitted. "The Fletchers are away, but there are lights on at the Desmonds'. You could call Mabel Desmond, Kim. If necessary, I mean."

"Phooey!"

Mabel Desmond is an old actress who used to be in the movies long ago. In the silent movies. Nobody ever calls her Mrs. Desmond. They always use her full name. Mother says she was famous in the old days. But I certainly wouldn't need *her*.

"I know more about taking care of a six-year-old than Mabel Desmond!" I said.

"Now, Kim," Mother said, as if I had criticized the woman. "Mabel Desmond is a very admirable person." Mabel Desmond has a look that Mother calls "faded grandeur." She wears a hat and gloves to the supermarket. White gloves all mended in the fingers. And although she's old, she sails along like a ship, her earrings swinging like lanterns.

"You've got to give her credit," Mother said. "They have so little and she puts on such a brave front. Their house is a shambles, but to hear her talk, you'd think it was a mansion."

"Fine mansion," Daddy laughed, "with cats in all the chairs."

It sounded to me as if "putting on a brave front" was just another kind of lying. Lying to yourself. I was getting to know quite a variety of different kinds of lies.

"Are we going or not!" Sherry wailed. She pulled her long hair free of her coat collar. "I've got to be there early."

So Mother finally put on her hat. It's of shaggy fur the same color as her hair. I'm always afraid someone will think she has an enormous head.

"All right, Kim," she said. "Perhaps we'll call up during intermission to make sure you're all right."

"Oh, *Mother*. We'll be fine."

"And if you *should* go to the Desmonds', please be tactful. Mind your manners."

"Honestly, Mother!" That made me think of old ladies holding teacups. *Mind your manners.* Or of little boys going to dancing school.

"Manners," Mother said, pulling on her gloves, "simply means thinking of others. If

54

you thought of others, you wouldn't *need* manners. You'd *have* them."

"Come *on*," Sherry said again. The show wasn't supposed to start until eight-thirty, but the cast had to be there at seven to get made-up and all. Mother and Daddy were going to drop her off and then do some last-minute shopping before the play started. Mother seemed to have given up the idea of an old-fashioned Christmas with just homemade gifts. That was fine with me. I didn't exactly want homemade figure skates.

Mother gave us the usual warnings and went to the door. Daddy was jiggling the car keys impatiently. "Be good, Peter. Don't give Kim any trouble." As if he ever would!

Then they were really gone. I was in charge of Peter and the house. I was responsible. I had a lot of plans. I was going to make a few Christmas cards. And I was going to surprise Mother by making the Christmas Eve cookies. We always leave some near the fireplace with a note saying, "Help yourself, Santa." That's for Peter's benefit, of course. He always looks at that plate the first thing, Christmas morning. And, of course, there's never anything left but crumbs. That was one of the good things about having a little brother. Someone in the family who still believed in Santa Claus made Christmas more fun for all of us.

Peter brought his crayons and a pad into the kitchen. "Let's color," he said.

"You start. I want to make a phone call."

Chapter 7

BEFORE DIALING ALISON'S number, I did
some thinking. I knew Alison missed me. At
school she was always calling other kids "Kim"
by mistake. I had even heard Patty Jo say,
"Alison, will you please stop calling me Kim!"
That showed Alison was thinking of me. But
she had made a vow not to speak to me, and I
knew from experience, you can't break a vow
without feeling crummy.

So how could I keep her from hanging up the minute she knew who was calling?

I know! I thought. I won't say, "This is Kim." I'll just say, "Guess what? I'm baby-sitting." Alison will be too surprised to hang up. She'll be thinking, "*I've* never had a baby-sitting job, and I'm two months older than Kim." So before she has time to remember her vow, I'll say, "How about coming over and baby-sitting with me? Then we'll both be experienced. We'll be able to get outside jobs as sitters and earn lots of money."

That ought to turn her on. But if it doesn't, if she doesn't agree right away, I'll tell her my idea about letting our nails grow long and cutting them into deadly points and calling ourselves "The Tigers." All our enemies — kids like Roberta Lawson — would be afraid of us. We'd never have to scratch anybody. We'd just show them our hands. Alison will probably say, "Kim, you get more ideas!" And then we'd be friends again.

Mother had been saying for weeks that I ought to apologize. But you can't call somebody up two weeks later and say, "I'm sorry I said you were ugly." It would just make them mad all over again. I liked Daddy's idea better. He said that all it needed was "one friendly gesture."

I picked up the phone and put it down again. What if Mrs. Morse answered? Alison's mother had told somebody I was the rudest child she had ever known.

Well, if Mrs. Morse answered, I'd disguise my voice. I'd say, "Hallo? Oskar? Diss iss Olga." I can do funny accents.

But that would be a lie, and I'd sworn never to lie again. Was I going to break my pledge just because of Mrs. Morse? I'd see, I thought, and reached for the phone. Before I could dial, it rang.

"Hallo? Diss is Oskar," I said, confused.

"What? Is that you, Kim?" Patty Jo asked. "What's the matter? You sounded so funny. Do you want to come caroling?"

"Who else is going?" I asked, meaning, "Is Alison going?"

"Me and Alison and Tommy Grimes, so far. We're going to ask Glenn and Martin Walker. If they come we'll need another girl."

"Well, I'm baby-sitting." It made me feel older, just saying it. "So I can't go. But why don't you stop by and say hello?"

The minute we'd hung up I felt lonesome. I hated to think of Alison out there without me. When the kids came by, I'd ask Alison to stay. She'll be cold and the kitchen will be warm and smell inviting, I thought. I mixed up some cookie dough and began to feel better.

Peter was sprawled under the table with his crayons.

"Isn't it too dark down there?" I asked.

"I like it," Peter said. "It's nice and shady."

Shady. In the kitchen. He kills me. Baby-sitting was fun, I thought. Not that other kids would be as nice to take care of as Peter. He's so funny. He's not perfect, of course. He can be stubborn at times. When he gets an idea, you can't shake it. For instance, he won't wear matching socks. He likes to wear one color on one foot and another on the other. He gets furious if you try to make him wear two alike. So Mother lets him have it his way. "It's not that important," she says.

And then he insists that his favorite color is black. Black. It's not even a color. I leaned down to see what he was doing. "What are you making?"

"A present for Santa Claus — a picture of himself."

"That's nice. We can leave it with the cookies." It was a pretty good picture, for a little kid. But when he started filling in the color, I saw he was making the suit black.

"Santa's suit should be red," I told him.

"I like black," Peter insisted. "Anyway, this is his good suit. His red is for every day."

I didn't argue. Let him do it his way, I thought. The bell of the oven timer went ting! At the same time the telephone rang.

"Get that, will you, Peter? And if it's for me, I'll be there in two secs." I didn't want the cookies to get too dark.

The call was for Peter, anyway. I heard him say, "Hi, Kenny." I put the cookies (peanut butter, my favorite) on a cooling rack. They looked good and smelled delicious. If they hadn't been too hot, I would have eaten one right then.

Peter was on the phone for quite a while. When he came back, he picked up the drawing he'd just made and crumpled it.

"Peter! What's the idea? That was nice."

"Not going to put it out," he said, his lips tight and stubborn. "There isn't any Santa Claus."

I felt as if somebody had punched me in the stomach. "How did you...who says so?"

"Kenny."

Kenny, whose information was always correct. Kenny, who knew about tachometers and altimeters and how fast birds fly.

"Is there?" he asked.

I didn't know what to say. We had always had fun talking about Santa Claus, pretending we heard his sleigh bells and his reindeer stamping. I pretended to be too busy to answer, washing the cookie sheet for the next batch of cookies.

I wanted to say, "Of course there's a Santa Claus!" But I'd be breaking my pledge. And making a liar out of Kenny, too. But if I told him the truth, Peter would lose Santa Claus forever. There wouldn't be a second chance.

"Well, is there?" Peter asked again.

"You wait and ask Daddy."

"Why? Don't you know?"

"Of course I do, silly."

"Then why don't you tell me?"

I wished I knew what Mother and Daddy would want me to say. "Didn't Mommy just help you write a letter to Santa Claus?"

"Yes."

"Well, then! Who are you going to believe — Mommy or some little kid?" That was a mistake. Kenny wasn't "some little kid." Peter felt about him the way I felt about Alison.

I was in such a jam I broke my pledge without thinking. "I once heard of a boy who didn't believe in Santa Claus, and he didn't get anything for Christmas."

"Not anything? What was his name? He could have my old fire truck. Where does he live, that boy?"

I banged the cookie sheet on the sink. "Peter, you're going to drive me up the wall with all those questions."

He looked hurt. I'd never yelled at him before. "Don't be mad, Kim. Just tell me if there's a Santa Claus."

"All right, there isn't. There isn't, there isn't. Now are you satisfied?"

He was, apparently. "I knew it. Kenny was right." He went to his room. I leaned against the refrigerator. I'd done it. I'd told him. When Mother and Daddy came home, they'd bawl me out, saying I should have been more tactful. I wanted to call Peter and take it all back. But that wouldn't work. Once something is said there isn't any way to take it back.

I'd found that out, with Alison. I felt miserable.

Chapter 8

I SANK DOWN on a chair. I had a real problem. But there was no use calling anyone. No one could help me with this kind of problem. Not even Alison, though I would have been glad to have her company.

Well, no use brooding. The damage was done. Christmas would never be the same for Peter after this. I remembered how you felt when you still believed in Santa Claus. You went to bed with a shivery, excited feeling, hoping he would come while you were asleep.

Then early, early in the morning, before it was really light, you slipped out of bed and ran to the living room and your heart almost stopped. Because he *had* been there! There was the tree, where nothing had been before, shimmering in the morning light, with mysterious packages on clouds of tissue paper underneath. The tree was more beautiful at that moment — shiny and silvery in the half-light — than it ever was afterward. I haven't had that shivery feeling in years.

It was a shame to have Peter lose it so soon. But what weighed like a stone on my chest was the fact that I had told him when maybe I needn't have.

He came in with his old fire truck, smelled the cookies, and asked for one. "I'm hungry."

"No," I said automatically. "Those are for Sa..." I had forgotten. "Here. You can have two." They were cool by now.

No sense saving them. There would be no sense in most of the things we did at Christmastime. I made a feeble attempt to right the situation.

"You know, Peter, when it comes to things

like Santa Claus, no one's really sure."

"Kenny is. Kenny says if you stay awake on Christmas Eve, all you'll hear is your mother and father talking. He says nobody could get around the whole world that way, stopping to give things to all the kids, in just one night."

"Maybe Santa uses a jet," I said foolishly.

"Besides, Kenny says chimneys are real small. Nobody with a fat stomach could get down a little chimney." Peter went to the living room and looked up the fireplace flue. "Wow. Is that tiny!"

Okay, I thought. I give up. I had tried.

A knock sounded at the kitchen door, and Patty Jo called, "Kim? Here we are."

I opened the door. "Can't you come with us, Kim?" Patty Jo asked. "If we can get you and one more, we'll have a double quartet."

Four boys, one of them quite small, were standing on the road, holding song sheets. Alison was waiting for Patty Jo, halfway between the boys and our house. Our big front light shone along the path, and I could see her clearly. Her cheeks were bright pink from the cold, and there were snowflakes stuck to her dark hair and eyelashes. Her face was framed with the white furry stuff that lined her hood. She looks pretty, I thought. I never knew Alison was so pretty. She caught me looking at her and turned away.

"I'm baby-sitting, Patty Jo," I said, speaking in a loud voice. "So I'm afraid I can't come. I'm getting experience sitting with my brother so I can earn money sitting for other people. And I'm having fun making cookies."

I could only hope Alison would get the message. In case she didn't, I added, "I wanted to call someone up and ask if they wanted to keep me company and get experience themselves."

"None of us can," Patty Jo said. "We haven't enough people for caroling as it is. Hey! Why don't you bring Peter? Then we'd have eight. Kenny's going."

I hadn't got through to Alison at all. She was scraping snow into a mound with her boot. "Kenny's older than Peter," I snapped. I wasn't really mad at them, but I must have sounded mad because Patty Jo said, "Okay," and they all went on.

I had felt a little lonesome before, now I suddenly felt like the only person on a desert island. I stood at the door wishing I could go with them, wishing I hadn't offered to baby-sit, wishing I hadn't told the truth about Alison's haircut. I even wished for a tiny second that I didn't have a little brother.

It looked beautiful out. The sky was black, with no stars. The snow that blanketed everything was untouched, except for footprints that led to our door and away again. I could hear an occasional voice from the pond, and the hollow scrape of skate blades. Some of the grownups who didn't have kids in the play must have been skating. I wished I could be with them. I love to skate when there's just an inch of fresh snow on the ice. Your skates go whispering through it, leaving black lines behind you like a signature.

When the phone rang, I went inside, slamming the door. I didn't feel like bragging about baby-sitting to anybody. Now I didn't consider it such a great thing any more. Everybody else was out having fun. I was stuck inside trying to answer questions. For a moment, talking to Patty Jo, I had forgotten my problem. Coming back to the kitchen and seeing the crumpled drawing of Santa Claus brought the unpleasant problem back to mind. I kicked the ball of crumpled paper and picked up the phone. It was Mother.

"What is it?" she asked, the minute I'd said hello. "Is something wrong?"

"No, we're fine." It would be a relief to tell her Peter's discovery, to ask for advice. But she would probably bawl me out. "Is it intermission?" I asked, thinking, only another hour and they'll be home.

"Heavens, no. We just got back from shopping. The play is going to start any minute. I just wanted to see how everything was."

"Everything's fine," I lied. I'd already broken my record anyway. And it had been such a great record — going all that time without even the teeniest fib.

"Are you sure? Where's Peter? What's he doing?"

"He's right here. With his fire truck." He'd be asleep when they got home so I could wait and tell them then.

"Are you feeling all right, Kim? Your voice sounds a little funny."

I could hear the kids singing at the Desmonds':

> O, little town of Bethlehem
> How still we see thee lie

"The kids are out caroling. They wanted me to come."

"So that's it!" I could hear the relief in Mother's voice. "Why didn't you say so? Listen, Kim, you can go out and sing with them if you like. It's not late."

"And leave Peter alone?"

"Of course not! Take him along. He'll enjoy it. He loved going out on Halloween. But don't go too far. He'll get tired. Just go as far as the Metzgers' and come back. All right?"

"Terrific!"

"But bundle up warm. It's cold out."

"We will."

"And don't lock yourself out."

"We won't. Bye."

I ran to Peter's room. He was almost upside down in his toy box, looking for the fire truck's lost wheel.

"Come on, Peter. We're going caroling." I pulled his snowsuit from the closet.

"I don't want to. What's caroling?"

"Singing Christmas carols. It's fun. You go from door to door, like Halloween."

His face brightened. "Like Trick or Treat?"

"Yes, only we don't get any candy."

"I don't want to go."

"Kenny's going. He's already started."

In one second flat Peter had thrown down the fire truck and was pulling on the pants of his snowsuit. That's all it takes, I thought. Just those few words and he changes his mind. Words were certainly powerful, when you thought about it. They could change a situation just like that. *Yeah*, I thought heavily. *They certainly could.* They could make your best friend hate you.

I helped Peter with his jacket, mittens, and boots, grabbed my own jacket, and we started out. Passing the kitchen door, I remembered the oven was still on and turned off the gas. Only one batch of cookies made. Daddy's suggestion, "one friendly gesture," popped into my mind. I'd give the cookies to Alison! I dumped them into a plastic bag, and we dashed out.

Chapter 9

"WOW ISN'T THIS great?" I shouted as I dragged Peter down the path to the road. I felt like someone who'd escaped from prison. I thought the night was the most beautiful I had ever seen. Every house had a different kind of decoration. At the Lorimers', the post light was wound with greenery and red ribbon. The singers were grouped before the front door,

their breath making frosty plumes as they sang.

"Wait! We're coming!" I called, pulling Peter through the snow. I hadn't stopped to put on snow pants or boots myself. My legs were cold by the time we passed the Fletchers'. My shoe- laces had come undone, and the metal tips stung my ankles as we ran to catch up. But I didn't care. It was wonderful to be out.

We reached the kids just as they finished the song, and I held out the plastic bag. I suddenly felt shy about giving them to Alison. How can you hand a present to someone who won't talk to you? "Here. They're just out of the oven."

"You made it," Patty Jo said. "I thought you couldn't come."

"She made *them*," Glenn Walker corrected, opening the bag and helping himself.

"I thought I might as well bring them."

"Good thinking, Agent 009," Glenn said with his mouth full. "Peanut butter. Full of pro- tein."

Alison gave us each a song sheet without say- ing anything. Peter looked at the mimeo- graphed sheet as if he could read it.

We sang "The First Noel" and ran on to the next house. The snow was letting up. It spiraled down a flake at a time in slow motion.

This was more fun than Halloween, I thought, even if there was no candy.

The big boys fell behind. The little kids ran ahead. That left us three girls together. I didn't care if Alison wasn't talking to me. "Isn't this fun!" I said. Peter and Kenny were pelting each other with snow. It fell from their mittens like handfuls of feathers. I felt light as a feather myself. In a minute or two, Alison was going to give up and say something. I was sure of it.

The Overtons had blue lights strung up and down the evergreens on both sides of their doorway. Alison looked at me and smiled, "Your face is all blue. Patty Jo," she added, remembering.

"Yours is, too," I answered, to show her I hadn't been fooled.

We sang "It Came Upon a Midnight Clear" and ran off calling "Merry Christmas," when the Overtons came to the door.

Peter and Kenny weren't much use as part of a double quartet. They didn't know the words and giggled more than they sang. Kenny rolled his song sheet into a cone and scooped up some snow. He licked it like an ice-cream cone and offered it to Glenn.

"No, thanks," Glenn said. "I don't like vanilla. I only like pumpernickel fudge."

"Pumpernickel fudge!" Kenny shrieked. He and Peter kept repeating it, laughing and falling down in the snow.

"That and spaghetti mint," Glenn said.

They repeated that, falling to their knees with laughter.

"Or maybe pizza walnut," Glenn said. "Or marshmallow chicken."

The little kids were giggling so much they couldn't stand up. I hoped Peter wouldn't wet his pants. He scooped up some snow on his music sheet and took it to Glenn on his hands and knees.

"Just what I wanted," Glenn told him. "Oatmeal ripple."

We were all laughing. We had to stop to catch our breath before going on.

At the Willoughbys' gold-wreathed door we sang "We Three Kings of Orient Are," trying to be serious because Christmas carols really are hymns. Then we trooped on to the next house.

Kenny studied the snow on his mitten under the Metzgers' porch light. "Know how many different shaped snowflakes there are?" he asked Peter. "Thousands. Millions. Maybe trillions. Because each one is different. Right, Martin?"

"Right on," Martin said.

"If you look at snowflakes through a microscope, you'll see that each snowflake is different. Right, Glenn?"

"Right," his brother answered.

"I'm getting a microscope for Christmas," Kenny told Peter. "I'll let you look through it."

"What's that?" Peter asked.

"A microscope is a gadget with a powerful lens," Martin explained. "You put something small, like a hair or a seed, under the lens; and it makes it look big so you can see what it's really like, how it's formed and all."

No wonder Kenny knew so much, I thought. His brothers took time to explain things.

Alison and Patty Jo were trying to decide what song to sing.

"Let's sing about Round John," Peter begged. Nobody knew what he was talking about, of course. I told them that I had explained again and again that the words were "round yon virgin," but that Peter kept forgetting. So we sang "Silent Night," and it sounded lovely.

After that, Peter and I had to leave. The others were going on, to all the houses around the pond.

"So long, Kim," Glenn said as we left.

"Thanks for the food. Only next time bring pumpernickel fudge, will you?"

"I'll do that. Good-by, everybody. Good-by, Alison."

"Good-by," they all chorused. Alison said it along with the others. That was something, I thought. We walked away.

We had gone about ten feet when a snowball hit me in the back. "Hey!" Martin said. "See you at the party." He liked me. That was a surprise. I liked him, too. Only Glenn was funnier. But even so, I felt deflated, like a balloon with the air suddenly gone out. I couldn't look forward to the party, because it wouldn't be the same.

Every year at Squires' Park Hall, there's a Christmas party for kids twelve and under. Santa Claus comes "in person," and it's a big thrill for the little kids. I always had to take Peter. But I never minded. I usually had a ball. And this year, because it was Alison's first Christmas party at Squires' Park, I had been especially looking forward to going. We would go together, I'd been thinking, and now she'd be going with Patty Jo. And it wouldn't be fun for Peter either this year. He'd know that Santa was a put-on, somebody's uncle or grandfather, dressed up.

I scuffed the snow as we trudged home. My shoes were soaked and my feet were freezing. So were my knees. Peter had raced ahead and was waiting at our path. He held up a handful of snow.

"Kenny says there are millions of shapes of snowflakes. You can see them if you look through a microscope. I'm going to ask Santa Claus to bring me a micro..." He broke off with a sheepish smile. "I forgot there isn't any Santa Claus."

"Oh, Peter!" I wailed. He didn't realize that everything was ruined, but I did. I suddenly felt angry. Angry with my parents, with all parents who tell their kids stuff that isn't true. I'd been blaming Martin and Glenn for spilling the beans. They weren't to blame. Why shouldn't they tell Kenny the truth! Dumb parents! I thought. Don't they know kids are going to find out?

I kicked a laurel bush and a shower of snow came down on our heads. "Do it again!" Peter said, delighted.

I stamped to the front door and then turned away. I just didn't want to go in. "Let's go say hello to the Desmonds." Anything seemed better than going home.

"I don't want to."

"Come on. They're our neighbors. We ought to be nice."

"I don't want to."

I sniffed the air. "She must be making brownies," I said as if to myself. "I smell chocolate." I'd been making that up, at first, to get Peter to come with me. But now I really did smell chocolate. I guess that was what put it in my mind. I had started toward the house next door.

"Wait," Peter called. He came running along, slipping and falling and getting up again. I went to take his hand.

As we reached the porch a striped cat rose from an old wicker rocker and stood at the door, waiting to go in. There was a pine branch on the door, tied with a frayed red ribbon. It was a change, anyway, from all the wreaths.

Peter's nose was running. I found a tissue in my pocket and used it on him. Then I lifted the knocker. It made a louder noise than I had expected.

"Maybe they're sleeping," I whispered. "Let's go."

Just then the door was thrown open.

Chapter 10

PETER TOOK MY hand rather nervously. I couldn't blame him. Mrs. Desmond is a very different-looking person. She's tall for a woman—what Mother calls "statuesque"— and tonight she looked taller than usual. She had her gray hair done high on her head and was wearing something long. She had on big green earrings and her eyelids were painted to match.

"Come in! Come in!" she invited. "Have the others gone?" She peered past us. "When I heard the singing I started a pot of cocoa. Very well, Victoria," she said to the striped cat, "you may come in, too."

She stepped aside, and the cat slipped in. "Won't you children come help me drink my cocoa? It only needs heating up."

"I will," Peter smiled up at her. It doesn't take much to win his approval.

"Good. Come in and close the door, dear. This tea gown is not very warm."

Tea gown! It looked like a faded old bathrobe to me, except that it was velvet. She held up one side as if it were a train, keeping it out of the way of the snow we brought in.

"Would you like some slippers?" she asked, looking at my wet shoes. "You'll find a pair in the library."

The room she waved toward was a living room like ours except that there wasn't much furniture. It did have two bookshelves but they held more cats than books. Some were curled up, some were washing themselves, others were stretching or scratching. I saw a pair of fur-lined slippers near an old leather chair, and though they were huge, they felt good. Peter had taken off his snowsuit in the hall and

was patting a cat. It purred like a percolator. I went to the kitchen, carrying my shoes.

"Put them there, by the register," Mabel Desmond said. A grating in the floor gave off heat. I stood near it. "I love this season!" she exclaimed, holding a wide sleeve out of the way as she stirred a pot of cocoa. "All tinsel and lights and make-believe. Just like the world of the theater. That's our world, you know, Mr. Desmond's and mine."

"Where is Mr. Desmond?" We sometimes saw him raking the yard, an old white-haired man with apple cheeks. I wondered if the slippers were his.

"He's at rehearsal!" she said, beaming.

"Rehearsal! He's going to be in a show?" Mr. Desmond was about eighty. My parents said he hadn't had a part in years.

"Not in a show, dear. He's going to appear at the Community Hall for the Christmas party. He's going to be..." Mabel Desmond glanced toward the hall. Peter was still there with the cat. She gave me a wink and said, "Edward is going to be the star performer, if you know what I mean. He's playing the leading role. They asked if he would do it this year, and he was delighted. He'll give a fine performance, as you'll see for yourself. He's there now, trying on his costume."

So that was it. Mr. Desmond was going to be Santa Claus at the Christmas party. And she didn't want Peter to know. He was lying down out there with one hand on the cat. He might have been asleep. But it didn't matter. As long as he knew there was no Santa Claus, he might as well know that the Santa who came to the Hall every year was just a man dressed up.

"So Mr. Desmond is going to be there in a Santa Claus suit." It seemed worse, somehow, to have it be the man next door.

"Yes, and beautifully made-up," she said. "Wait till you see his beard. No false beard for Edward. He'll use real crepe hair as he did for King Lear, and glue it on a strand at a time."

"Making it look real so he can fool the little kids!" I didn't care if I *was* brutally frank.

"But my dear, that's an actor's job. Not to fool people, but to create an illusion, for their enjoyment. Edward has played King Richard III and the king in *Hamlet*, as well."

"Santa Claus isn't a king. He's just a…"

"A legend," Mabel Desmond supplied. "A legendary character, and a beautiful one. We must have our myths and legends, you know, stories that have come down through generations."

"Myths aren't true," I said, thinking of the one about George Washington.

"Heavens above! If we had to live with nothing but the truth, how dull that would be! We'd have no plays, no movies."

I'd never thought of that. If people only wrote true stories there wouldn't be any books like *Alice in Wonderland* or *The Wind in the Willows* or *Charlotte's Web*.

The cocoa rose to the top of the pot. Just when it was about to boil over Mabel Desmond blew on the bubbles, and they subsided. She turned off the gas.

"Some legends are based on truth," she said. "St. Nicholas, you know, was an actual person."

"He was? You mean there really was a man who went around…"

She nodded. "St. Nicholas was a third-century bishop who was known for giving gifts. In the Netherlands, he was proclaimed the patron saint of children. He was called Sante Niklasse there. The name gradually became Santa Claus."

"Hey, that's neat." I said it over a few times. "Sante Niklasse. St. Nicholas. Santa Claus." Only it didn't matter what they called him, as far as we were concerned. Peter and the cat were stretched out in the hall. The cat's purring sounded like somebody snoring. "You know what? Peter just found out there isn't any Santa Claus." It helped to tell somebody, even if it was only Mabel Desmond.

"I see," she said, stirring the cocoa and dropping three marshmallows in the pot. "How old is he?"

"Only six."

"And you? How old are you?"

"Eleven."

"Eleven!" Mabel Desmond repeated it in the tone you might use saying, "Daffodils!" in the spring. "How delightful."

"It wasn't exactly delightful," I muttered, "to be the one to tell him." And then, so she wouldn't blame me for blabbing, I told her what had happened after Kenny's phone call, and how awful I'd felt ever since.

"My dear child, you did the right thing!" she pronounced, like a judge handing down a decision. "Your brother trusts you. Surely it would have been wrong to betray that trust."

I could have hugged her. It was just what I'd been wanting to hear.

"That's what *I* think. People should tell the truth," I said. "But my mother doesn't think so. I told this friend of mine, Alison Morse, that her short haircut made her look ugly, and Mother practically had a heart attack. And it was true. That dumb haircut made Alison's ears stick out like the handles on a sugar bowl."

Mabel Desmond didn't approve this time. "We don't want to look so hard at the handles that we miss the sugar in the bowl."

That made me think a minute. "Well, Alison did look nicer before. She had beautiful long hair. I thought if I didn't tell her, she'd keep it short and go on looking ugly forever. She was my best friend, and now she won't talk to me."

"Yes," Mabel Desmond sighed. "When we like people we resent any change. Why not tell your friend how you truly feel? About her, I mean, not her hair. Oh, I know. It's difficult. The most difficult thing to be truthful about is our feelings, even with those close to us. We hide them. Or even say the opposite of what is so."

She was a fine one to talk about being truthful, I thought. Calling an old bathrobe a tea gown, and a bare living room, a library. Still, I guess putting on a "brave front," as Mother says, is just a way of making the best of things, and that *is* brave.

Peter came in carrying the striped cat. "I'm hungry."

"Yes, Milord." Mabel Desmond dropped a

dignified curtsy. "You shall have the first cup." She walked to a cupboard, lifting the hem of her robe above the dishes of cat food that lay here and there on the worn linoleum. "Let's make it a party and use the good bone china, shall we?"

She took three cracked, gold-rimmed cups from their hooks. The cocoa foamed into them. The windows fogged with steam. We drank silently.

"That was good." Peter gave a tremendous, cocoa-encircled yawn.

"I'd better get him home." I helped Peter with his snowsuit, put on my jacket and my cold, wet shoes.

"Thanks for the lend of the slippers."

"Thanks for the cocoa," Peter said.

"You're quite welcome. Come again. Good night."

"Good night. Merry Christmas," we called from the porch.

"She's nice," Peter said as we walked away. "If her husband is a king, then she must be a queen—right?"

"I guess so." She was like a queen, I thought. She'd be good as the fairy godmother in *Cinderella*.

Chapter 11

THE SKY WAS like black velvet, the snow like sparkling white fur. The night was still. I could no longer hear skates on the pond or the carolers singing.

Alison would be home, I thought, as we ran down the path to our own house. If it wasn't too late, maybe I could call her and do as Mrs. Desmond had suggested. "Alison," I would say, "I miss you."

It would be hard. I'd feel silly. Mabel Desmond was right when she said we hide our feelings. Alison and I had said we hated boys. We didn't hate them at all. When Alison and Patty Jo walked with their arms around each other and whispered, I'd acted as if I didn't care. And I *did* care. Well, I'd go back to my truth kick and admit I hadn't had any fun since the Saturday after Thanksgiving. "Please, Alison," I'd say, "Can't we be friends again?"

But I had to get Peter to bed first. He was too tired to undress himself. His arms were as limp as strands of spaghetti as I helped him into his pajamas. I washed the cocoa from his face, and as soon as he was in bed, I dialed Alison's number.

Her grandmother answered. She had come for the holidays. "Alison is in bed. Is there any message?"

"No, thanks." I'd go see Alison the next morning and say it in person. That would be even harder, but it would be worth it. I was tired myself, but I couldn't go to bed until I had cleaned up the kitchen. I washed the spoons and measuring cups, covered the mixing bowl with foil, and picked up Peter's crayons. Mother and Daddy would be home soon. I'd have to tell them that Peter had found out about Santa Claus.

I decided to avoid the whole thing by going to bed. Let Peter tell them himself, I thought. He'd probably do so first thing in the morning. And if they didn't like it, it was their own fault. Parents shouldn't fool kids.

I turned on my side with my hand under the pillow, the way I always sleep. Suddenly I remembered what fun it was when I'd lost a tooth, to find a shiny dime or quarter under my pillow. What if Mother had said, "Leave your tooth under the pillow and *Daddy* will leave some money there." What fun would that have been? Not much. It was the idea of the fairy coming, of something mysterious happening in the night that was fun. The surprise. Maybe grownups weren't so bad, I thought sleepily. They weren't fooling kids, exactly. They were more — *hum* — I was too tired to keep my thoughts straight. Like Mabel Desmond said about actors — *hum* — another yawn. Enjoyment.

All Peter talked about at breakfast was the fun we had had going caroling. Right afterward, Mother sent him outside. Kenny came over and they started making a snowman. The minute Peter was out of hearing, Mother told me what they'd bought for him the night before.

"You know we got him trains — right after he asked for them in that letter to Santa Claus. Well, last night we got some extra things for his layout!"

"A station," Daddy said. "And a railroad bridge. I'm going to build a tunnel."

"Little trees," Mother added. "And street lamps that light up. I can't wait to see his face when he gets them."

After that I didn't have the heart to tell them about Kenny's call, so I went outside myself. The snowman was finished. Kenny put a branch next to the snowman's arm. "That's his cane." I found a skinny pine cone, and we stuck it in the snowman's mouth for a cigar. It looked good. We stood back to admire it. Two minutes later Peter and Kenny were whacking the snowman with their shovels, knocking it down just for fun. Boys! I thought.

"Anybody want to come for a walk?" I asked.

"Nope," they both said.

So I walked to Alison's alone. It had grown cold. The sky was gray. A sharp wind blew snow from the trees. It hit my face like handfuls of cold confetti. And all the way I kept wondering what I'd say if somebody else came to the door when I knocked. The grandmother I didn't know, or Alison's mother who had such

a bad opinion of me. I should have worn one of those knitted ski masks, I thought. Then they wouldn't know me.

The Morses' door was trimmed with a swag of ground-pine roping — just like ours. Our mothers had made the roping together. They were still friends. That ought to help.

I took a deep breath and rang the bell. "I'm sorry, Alison," I'd say. "I can't have any fun without you." Stuff like that. I could hear the chimes go inside. *Bong* bong, *bong* bong. For once I was lucky. Alison came to the door herself. But she was in her bathrobe. Sick! I thought, and all the things I'd planned to say went out of my head. I could take care of her, I thought (forgetting the grandmother), since Alison's mother worked, too, in a real estate office. I could take her temperature and bring her meals, and Mrs. Morse would say, *"You've pulled her out of it. How can we thank you?"*

"What's the matter?" I asked, while all that went through my head.

"Nothing. I'm getting ready for the party." At least she was talking to me.

"This early!"

"I have to take a bath and wash my h..." Her lips clamped shut. I could tell she had been going to say "wash my hair." Her cheeks turned red. I pretended not to notice.

"Well, it's not very nice out anyway." I waited for her to ask me to come in. When she didn't I suggested she come to my house after lunch. "You'll be all ready, and we could go to the party together."

"What would we do, all dressed up?"

"We could — we could play nurse. We could take turns being sick, just lying quietly on my bed, not getting our clothes mussed up. The one who's nurse can bring trays of tea and toast and stuff. We could have strange diseases. I can have mononucleosis and you can have sickle cell anemia."

"I don't know. My grandmother's here." Or maybe Alison hadn't decided whether to make up with me or not.

"Alison!" Mrs. Morse called. "Who is it?"

"Nobody," Alison answered.

"You can have mononucleosis," I offered, "if you'd rather, and I'll have sickle cell anemia."

"Alison!" We heard footsteps.

"I'd better go in," Alison said. "See you."

There was nothing to do but go home and have lunch and get ready for the party. Some party! I wondered what Peter and Kenny would do, now that they knew there wasn't any

Santa Claus. Would they go around making sneering remarks? Telling other little kids that Santa was just a man dressed up? The party was going to be a real drag this year. I asked Mother if I had to go.

"Why, of course! You wouldn't want to miss the Christmas party!"

Wouldn't I?

At a quarter to three Peter and I left for the Hall. It was snowing again, but this time in flakes so fine it was more like a mist. I was wearing the same party dress I'd worn last year, with the hem let down. But I had brand-new shoes with little heels. They made my boots slip, and I couldn't walk very fast. Peter kept running ahead and coming back for me.

For the past week there had been a sign on the Community bulletin board announcing the party. It was a picture of Santa Claus. Underneath it said, HI! I'LL SEE YOU AT THE HALL, SUNDAY AT 3:00. Tommy Grimes' father, who is an art director at an advertising agency, had painted it. The paper had buckled from the dampness. The paint had run like tears. And a lost mitten was tacked to one side. It made me feel sad.

Peter, however, was bouncing like a bunny.

He tugged at my hand. "Come on! He might be early."

I looked at his face, bright as a new penny, and it struck me that I'd done a lot of worrying for nothing. Peter was just as eager to see Santa Claus as before. Maybe more so. As a matter of fact, *he* hadn't been bothered by Kenny's phone call. *I* was the only one who had been. Peter had been happy all along, just as excited over Christmas as ever. Things hadn't been spoiled for him.

Suddenly it hit me. I knew what was wrong. I hadn't wanted Peter to grow up and get wise to things. As Mabel Desmond had said about Alison, when we like people a lot, we don't want them to change. I hadn't wanted Alison to change, either. I had liked her just the way she was.

But changing her hair style really didn't make Alison a different person. She just looked different.

Chapter 12

THE MINUTE I opened the door to the Hall I felt excitement spring up in me like a fountain. There was that wonderful Christmasy smell, for one thing. And the buzz and chatter of voices. The whole room was decorated. Evergreen branches along the mantle and over the windows. A Christmas tree at one end and at the other a high-backed chair on a platform like a throne, all covered with red velvet. Next to it was a table piled with Christmas stockings and small packages.

Peter threw off his jacket and ran to find Kenny. I took our coats to the cloak room and looked around. I didn't see Alison but Patty Jo was there with some cousins, a boy and a girl. She told me they had come to stay over the holidays.

The room began to fill up. In spite of my earlier misgivings, my stomach felt full of butterflies. Everybody was happy and excited. The whole place seemed to vibrate with anticipation. Like feeling jittery in a nice way.

"Santa's coming. He's coming," Mothers kept assuring little kids three and four and five years old. "He'll be here soon."

I saw Tommy Grimes and Martin and Glenn. They all said "Hi" and then Martin had to leave because the party was for kids twelve and under and he was thirteen. As he went to the door he said, "Hey, Kim, how about coming skating tonight? They're going to put flood lights on the pond."

"Fine," I said. Martin must really like me, I thought. And I liked him, too.

I turned around and there was Alison.

"I'll come if Alison will," I said quickly.

Martin nodded. "Glenn's coming. You come too, Alison. We'll have fun."

"Okay," Alison answered. She had on a red velvet dress. It was really nice, with a white lace collar. Only she had on red tights and red shoes and a red band on her hair. She looks like a nosebleed, I thought. But I remembered what Mabel Desmond had said about the sugar in the sugar bowl, and didn't say what I was thinking.

"Hi, Alison," I said. "You look pretty." (She did, from the knees up.) "I love your dress!"

Alison smiled. Then, before she could say anything, someone called out, "Here he comes!" Everybody rushed to the windows. Alison grabbed my hand. We dashed over and got a good place.

"There he is." Alison pointed to a hill at our left.

You had to look hard to see him. The snow was like a gauze curtain. The hill was some distance away. But there he was — a sturdy figure trudging over the rise. Red suit, red cap, black boots and a pack on his back, he looked exactly as I'd pictured him when I was little. And the snow made it perfect.

He raised a mittened hand in greeting, and the little kids screamed with excitement! I al-

most felt like screaming myself. It seemed for a minute that this was actually Santa Claus himself! The whole scene was so real and beautiful, like a Christmas card come to life.

The snow had stopped by the time we left the Hall. The sky was dark. Patty Jo waved from the car as she drove by with her cousins who had come for the holidays. She'd be busy with them. Alison and I would be together. We waved back.

We both agreed that it had been the best Christmas party ever. And I needn't have worried about Peter and Kenny. They had waited in line to see Santa, had sat on his knee and talked to him just as they had other years. I don't know what Peter said to him, but I saw him pat Santa's beard.

"That was a good Santa," Peter said now. He and Kenny were walking just ahead of us. The other boys were ahead of them.

"Yeah, he sure was," Kenny agreed.

"Know who it was?" Peter asked. "Mr. Desmond. Know how come he's got such a good beard? He glues it on a little at a time. Know what it's made of? Some kind of hair."

That was a switch. Peter was giving Kenny information for a change. Pretty smart of him to have remembered, I thought.

They stopped in front of the bulletin board, looking at the picture of Santa Claus. "Know what?" Peter said, "I think I'll believe in him, just until after Christmas."

"Me, too," said Kenny.

Alison and I looked at each other and smiled. I noticed that Peter was almost as tall as Kenny now. Last year Kenny had been half a head taller. Peter was growing fast. He'd grow out of being little and cute and funny. But he'd be smart. And a nice kid.

I was growing smarter myself. I felt I'd learned a lot in the past few weeks, though I hadn't sorted it all out in my mind. It was funny to think that it was for only a month that Alison and I hadn't been friends. It had seemed like a year.

We walked her home. At her door she took a tiny box from her pocket. "Here. Merry Christmas, Kim."

"For me? What is it?"

"Wait and see."

She ran into the house, and I walked on with the little kids. What in the world had she given me? I hadn't expected her to give me a present at all. Alison hadn't said, "Don't open till Christmas." I couldn't wait.

I let the boys go on without me and opened

the box. I lifted a piece of cotton and caught my breath. There was a little gold-colored pin in the shape of a dachshund. Its rhinestone eye twinkled like a diamond. It was every bit as cute as the one we had found — better, because it was brand-new. I ran home to show Mother.

"Wasn't that thoughtful of Alison," Mother said. "She must know how much you like dogs."

That wasn't all Alison knew about me. Suddenly my eyes grew hot. I couldn't feel perfectly happy, even with this wonderful present. Alison had picked exactly the right gift for me. I didn't have anything for her. And nothing I could buy would be as nice as this.

"We're friends again, anyway," I thought. "We can have our club."

Right then I got an idea. Instead of buying a present, I'd make a list of things we could do. New ways we could have fun. Things we could make. I'd put them in a notebook. And make up a language, too, and put that in. If I started right away, I could get it done in time for Christmas.

And on January first, I decided, I'd make a New Year's resolution: *To tell the truth, the whole truth, and nothing but the truth—with just a few tactful lies.*

THE GREEK ISLANDS
Genius Loci

View of Naxos island seen through the monumental doorway of the Archaic temple.
Thomas Hope (1769-1831) Watercolour, 44 x 29 cm. Benaki Museum, Inv. No. 27375.
© 2010 Benaki Museum, Athens.

Author's acknowledgements

This series of twenty books covering the Aegean Islands is the fruit of many years of solitary dedication to a job difficult to accomplish given the extent of the subject matter and the geography involved. My belief throughout has been that only what is seen with the eyes can trustfully be written about; and to that end I have attempted to walk, ride, drive, climb, sail and swim these Islands in order to inspect everything talked about here. There will be errors in this text inevitably for which, although working in good faith, I alone am responsible. Notwithstanding, I am confident that these are the best, most clearly explanatory and most comprehensive artistic accounts currently available of this vibrant and historically dense corner of the Mediterranean.

Professor Robin Barber, author of the last, general, *Blue Guide to Greece* (based in turn on Stuart Rossiter's masterful text of the 1960s), has been very generous with support and help; and I am also particularly indebted to Charles Arnold for meticulously researched factual data on the Islands and for his support throughout this project. I could not have asked for a more saintly and helpful editor, corrector and indexer than Judy Tither. Efi Stathopoulou, Peter Cocconi, Marc René de Montalembert, Valentina Ivancich, William Forrester and Geoffrey Cox have all given invaluable help; and I owe a large debt of gratitude to John and Jay Rendall for serial hospitality and encouragement. For companionship on many journeys, I would like to thank a number of dear friends: Graziella Seferiades, Ivan Tabares, Matthew Kidd, Martin Leon, my group of Louisianan friends, and my brother Iain— all of whose different reactions to and passions for Greece have been a constant inspiration.

This work is dedicated with admiration and deep affection to Ivan de Jesus Tabares-Valencia who, though a native of the distant Andes mountains, from the start understood the profound spiritual appeal of the Aegean world.

McGILCHRIST'S GREEK ISLANDS

6. MYKONOS AND DELOS

Nigel McGilchrist

GENIUS LOCI PUBLICATIONS
London

McGilchrist's Greek Islands Mykonos and Delos
First edition

Published by Genius Loci Publications
54 Eccleston Road, London W13 0RL

Nigel McGilchrist © 2010
Nigel McGilchrist has asserted his moral rights.

ISBN 978-1-907859-03-8

A CIP catalogue record of this book is available from the British Library.

The author and publisher cannot accept responsibility or liability for
information contained herein, this being in some cases difficult to verify
and subject to change.

Layout and copy-editing by Judy Tither

Cover design by Kate Buckle

Maps and plans by Nick Hill Design

Printed and bound in Great Britain by TJ International Ltd, Padstow, Cornwall

The island maps in this series are based on the cartography of
Terrain Maps
Karneadou 4, 106 75 Athens, Greece
T: +30 210 609 5759, Fx: +30 210 609 5859
terrain@terrainmaps.gr
www.terrainmaps.gr

This book is one of twenty which comprise the complete, detailed
manuscript which the author prepared for the *Blue Guide: Greece,
the Aegean Islands* (2010), and on which the *Blue Guide* was
based. Some of this text therefore appears in the *Blue Guide*.

CONTENTS

Mykonos

Armenistis Lighthouse

Fokos Bay

Panormos Bay

Le Profitis Elias
Anomeritis
341

Kalafati Bay

Frangia Bay

Dragonisi

Vorni Hill

Frigia (Neolithic Settlement)

Palaiokastro

Tourliani Monastery

Ano Mera

Tarsanas Point

New Port

Tourlos

Ag Pantéleimon

Museam

Tourlos Bay

Old Port

Mykonos

Mykonians
Toulo Tomb

Ornos

Airport

Vino
Hellenistic
Towers

Algrys
Gialos

Elia Bay

Rheumatiari Islets

Sanctuary of Apollo
(see detailed maps)

Mt Kynthos
112

Delos

Sanctuary of Hercules
& Ancient Settlement

Bay of Aghia Triada

Purification
Pit

Rheneia

0   1   2   3km

N

Based on TERRAIN MAPS cartography
www.terrainmaps.gr

MYKONOS

Mykonos is a legend, in more ways than one. The transformation of a dry, knotty, granitic island of dour sailors and fisherfolk into the plush Mykonos of today is the stuff of legend. Nobody could have foreseen it a century ago, or predicted that this waterless and windswept island, well-known for its harshness since Antiquity, would become a home to almost 10,000 people, with twice as many guests in addition during the summer, served by two harbours and an airport that never seem to know a moment's pause in the season. Then there are the other legends: the nightlife, the gay life, the beaches, the international cuisine, and the fashion parades of Europe's jetset. It must be said that the frenzy of the 70s and 80s is largely over, and Mykonos has now settled into being a well-ordered, up-market tourist destination. Out of season it can be a delight, and only a reflex prejudice could blind one to the beauty of the Chora's curving harbour and the houses stacked behind, as seen from the sea on arrival. The experience of visiting Mykonos, however, is necessarily very different from that of other islands. It has become a place for those who desire their Greek island to be an extension of the city—cosmopolitan, busy, materially well-provided, a place to show off new clothes. For many temporary residents, Mykonos is a background, a pretty vessel into which to transpose the familiar routines (and problems) of prosperous suburbia—shopping, ethnic cuisine, luxury cars, searching for a parking place, and creating improbable gardens of imported exotic plants watered with imported water. Mykonos is never dull: for the student of humanity there is ample scope for reflection. With the fading of every riotous Saturday night into the dawn of a new Sunday, as the tables are being finally cleared at some of the more colourful of the island's bars around the church of Aghia Kyriaki, the silver-haired septuagenarian ladies of Mykonos, dressed in black, some with their wind-eroded husbands, are already gathering for a liturgy at the church in the cool of the morning. It is an encounter of two worlds, with nothing at all in common. But it continues undisturbed, and on Mykonos both worlds are felt more intensely through the proximity of the other.

The story of the island's past is told amply in the Chora's several excellent museums of folklore, and of maritime and rural life. The intractability of their land forced generations of islanders from Mykonos to seek an existence on the seas by trade or by piracy; the women folk who stayed on shore did most to manage the meagre agricultural productivity and animal husbandry. That there was energy and time to spare on top of this to build the 800 or so chapels and churches on the island, that seem to sprout from every rock, is remarkable. Mykonos has no tradition of wall-paintings in its churches, but the carved wooden icon screens, often coloured, within the plain interiors are a beautiful adornment. And the simple and enduring logicality of the Chora's cubic, balconied houses has been an inspiration to modern architects as diverse as Adalberto Libera and Le Corbusier.

HISTORY AND LEGEND

Underneath Mykonos, according to myth, lie buried the last of the giants who had contested the Olympian gods and were finally destroyed by the rocks hurled by Hercules: the landscape is indeed granitic and boulder-strewn. Despite its infertility, man settled on Mykonos in the 5th millennium BC; settlements have been found at Fteliá in Panormos Bay, and at Kalafáti. There was some continuity through the Early and Middle Cycladic periods, and the recent discovery of the tomb of a Mycenaean nobleman near Chora attests a significant Late Bronze Age presence. In historic times, according to Scylax of Caryanda, the island had two cities, *Mykonos* on the site of the present

Chora, and (?) *Panormos* on the north coast. The Persian commander, Datis, stopped at Mykonos in 490 BC on his way to Greece. After the Persian Wars the island became an Athenian colony. In ancient Comedy, the figure of the 'Μυκόνιος γείτων' or 'the neighbour from Mykonos' was the typical free-loader and uninvited guest. Strabo (*Geog.* X, 5.9) noted that baldness was prevalent on the island so that bald men were sometimes called 'Mykoniots': Henry A.V. Post observed the same when he visited in 1828.

At the time that Marco Sanudo established himself as 'Duke of Naxos' in 1207, Mykonos was taken by the Venetian Ghisi brothers who also held Tinos and the Sporades. The Ghisi line died out in 1390, and Tinos and Mykonos were bequeathed to Venice who put the administration of the islands up for auction in 1406, with a leased governorship which was renewed every four years; but in 1430 this system gave way to direct rule of the 'province of Tinos' from Venice, with governors directly appointed for two years. In 1537 Khaireddin Barbarossa took Mykonos. The island remained an Ottoman possession for almost 300 years, apart from an interval in which it was occupied by the Russians between 1770 and 1774. During the struggle for Greek Independence, the islanders repulsed an attack by the Turks in 1822 under the inspired leadership of the heroine Mando Mavrogenous. The island was united with the newly formed Greek State in 1830, after which the traditional skills of the islanders as mariners led Mykonos to prominence as a merchant-naval centre until the advent of the new generation of steamships. The boom in tourism beginning in the 1970s meant that the town tripled in size in the space of a little over two decades.

The guide to the island has been divided into two sections:
- *Mykonos Chora*
- *Around the island*

MYKONOS CHORA

Chora's labyrinth of tiny streets, deliberately tortuous so as to break the wind, seems confusing at first encounter. The plan, however, is not complicated: the main thoroughfare of the old part of Chora is in the form of a horseshoe which begins (as Matogianni Street) from the southeastern end of the main waterfront by the taxi stand, makes a deep loop south, turns west after 300m, passes the church of St George, and then heads back north (as Mitropoleos and Georgouli Streets) to the southwest corner of the waterfront again, not far from the *Demarcheion*, or town hall. This route passes the main shops and churches, and within its loop it embraces the oldest core of habitation— an area which remains miraculously untouched by even the fiercest wind. In the narrow strip between the west of the loop and the shore is the waterfront known as 'Little Venice'; at its southern end is the rise crowned with the famous windmills of Mykonos; at its northern end, is the low mound which was once the fort of the ancient and mediaeval town, whose principal remnant is the beautiful church of the Paraportianí. The architecture of the town speaks of the different social groups which inhabited the various areas; the lower class houses, clustered in the narrow alleys just behind the harbour, the upper middle-class houses (of which 'Lena's House'—*see below*—is a typical example) in the more spacious area at the southern end of the loop, and the ship-owner's houses with high-ceilings and balconies which form the front at 'Little Venice'.

THE KASTRO

We begin in the '**Kastro**' **area**, at the northwestern point of the town. The acropolis of Ancient *Mykonos* was a meagre hill—the area behind today's town hall—projecting from the centre of the west coast of the island, and marking a small harbour to its east. A Byzantine and then Venetian *kastro* succeeded it, of which scant remains can still be seen at the western extremity by the shore and in the cellars and lower floors of the buildings in the area. To the west, the **church of the Panaghía Paraportianí**, as its name implies, must have stood by the fortress's postern gate or '*paraporti*'.

This iconic building of Cycladic architecture is not one church but a curious agglutination of five chapels. Strictly speaking, the chapel of the Panaghía Paraportianí is the small 'oratory' under the dome on the upper floor; it is built on top of an earlier church beneath it, in the middle of the building, dedicated to the Aghii Anargyri (SS. Cosmas and Damian), and dating from the early 15th century; then a church of Aghia Anastasia has clung to the south, another dedicated to the Saviour (Aghios Sozon) to the northwest, and another dedicated to Aghios Efstathios to the east. The result of all this agglutination is a highly evocative profile—lively, organic, and different from every angle. The complex is supported by irregular stone buttresses, which, if not part of the actual walls of the former *kastro*, are reorganised material from them. It is a building created by happenstance—part ruin, part complete—whose disparate elements slowly come together as the building rises, into a harmonious, pyramidal form of uncertain outlines as if eroded by the sea around.

The nearby church of **Aghios Ioannis Vathous**, on the edge of the rocks to the north, still preserves a damaged wall-painting of the Archangel Michael in its interior, above the iconostasis. It also contains two late 17th century **icons** of great beauty by Michaïl Raphios. In the floor of the small church directly to the south, Aghia Soteira tou Kastrou, is the **grave of Manolis Mermelechas,** one of the most famous pirates of the Cyclades, who died of cholera on Mykonos in 1854. Some time around 1830, Mermelechas renounced his life of fearless pillage and became a bakery owner, living on Mykonos as an ordinary citizen until his death. The area of Kastro is dotted with other churches which have survived where the fortress itself has disappeared: of them all, **Aghios Demetrios** (east of the Paraportianí) is probably the oldest and dates from the 13th century. In the north wall of the interior of the church, which is composed of a main aisle and a side chapel, is a blind arcade supported by ancient columns with fine inverted Ionic capitals.

The 18th century sea-captain's house, which forms part of the northern border of the area overlooking the sea, houses a **Folklore Museum** (*open Easter–Oct daily 5.30–8.30pm*). This, together with the 'Lena's House' Museum (*see below*), gives an interesting picture of Mykoniot life of the 19th and early 20th centuries. The furniture, textiles, paintings and photographs recreate a typical 19th century interior: in the lower level there are exhibits of boats, rigging, naval cannon and other maritime material, as well as the so-called 'Well of Mermelechas' which must have been in service in the Venetian castle long before the time of the pirate.

The often windswept northern quay and main promenade of the town has been enlarged northwards into the area of the harbour; originally the tiny chapel of **Aghios Nikolaos tou Gialou** on its edge, stood on a small islet of rock accessible only by an arched bridge. The present Neoclassical structure is the last of many churches on the site, and dates from the early years of the 20th century. Facing it is the **Town Hall**, built in the late 18th century as a residence for the Russian consul, Count Ivan Voinovich, during the period of the Russo-Turkish War of 1768–74. In its portico are marble elements taken from Delos. Opposite and to the east, a fish-market takes place on the promenade in the early morning, regularly attended by the island's tame pelican who—although now in the umpteenth generation—is still always called 'Petros'. The tradition is an old one, and the independent traveller, Bernard Randolph, was intrigued by the island's pelicans when he came to Mykonos in the 1680s. He attempted to measure the seemingly bottomless capacity of the pouch of the beak, and found that it exceeded twelve quarts. Petros, who wanders freely through the town, can sometimes be encountered after dark, head under wings, asleep in the alleyways away from the noise of the nightlife.

From the promenade to Kato Myli and 'Little Venice'

The churches of Chora mostly date from the 17th and 18th centuries and although they have plain and undecorated walls, they are not without beauty. The variety of painted and carved wooden iconostases—such as in the double church of **Aghios Blasios and of the Metamorphosis**

(Transfiguration), founded in 1668 (*one block south of the centre of the promenade*)—as well as a number of the icons in the churches are of note. Set back from the town's west shore in a square which was once a boat-yard in mediaeval times, is a group of Chora's most important churches: the highly decorated Orthodox Cathedral of the **Panaghia Pigaditiótissa**, dedicated to the Zoödochos Pigi, with its ornate **wooden throne** of 1769, whimsically carved with hidden faces; and the rather more chaste Roman Catholic church of the Panaghia Rodariou, standing to its west. A broad flight of steps leads from the southwest corner of this square up to **Kato Myli** and the low hill crowned by seven windmills, five of which have been restored and now form part of a well-displayed, open-air **Museum of Agriculture**, dedicated to various aspects of the rural heritage of Mykonos and to the exploiting of the island's abundant winds to power mills for flour. There is evidence of windmills at Mykonos from as early as the 15th century.

Looking north from the hill of Kato Myli, the heterogeneous assemblage of façades of the ship-owners' houses in **Little Venice** stretches attractively below. Protruding first-floor, wooden verandas, supported on beams above the spray of breaking waves, allowed the owners to watch for the arrival of their vessels as they rounded the tip of Rhéneia.

The 'Tria Pigadia' area

Inland to the east of Kato Myli, at the southernmost point of the main thoroughfare is the church of **Aghios Giorgios**: the interior is divided by arches springing from a fluted classical column, truncated and surmounted by a capital. Opposite are the minuscule chapels of Aghia Barbara and Aghios Phanourios. This area is known as Tria Pigadia, 'three wells', and was once the town's crucial, and only, freshwater source.

Beside Aghios Giorgios is the **Museum of Lena's House** (*open Apr–Oct daily 6–9pm, Sun 6–8pm*)—understated, beautifully presented and perhaps, in the end, more instructive than the Folklore Museum in the *Kastro*. Lena Skorvanou died in the early 1970s: she was the unmarried daughter of a Mykoniot wood-merchant, engaged in an activity of millennial importance on Mykonos—bringing timber for boat building and roofing from the Black Sea to the wood-starved Cyclades. In a manner typical of the merchant classes at the turn of the 20th century, he studied in Paris and his son (Lena's brother) in Alexandria—something which explains the provenance of many of the items exhibited. The museum consists of only a part of the original house, a living-room and two bedrooms above (Lena's to left, and her parents' to right). Most of the furniture is French, some of it English. Lena's bed is

Viennese: kept above where she slept were the wedding-crown of her mother (Lena never married), and a hanging bottle of holy water, along with the icons which represented the religious and ancestral protection necessary to get through the night. By contrast with the wooden ceilings below, the roofs of the bedrooms were made in a traditional Cycladic fashion—woven with reeds, covered with a layer of seaweed, and bound in a 'cement' made with sand and crushed sea-shells which sealed it and created a terrace above. This endowed warmth in winter and conserved cool in summer. The garden and main reception room of Lena's house are now occupied by the **Aegean Maritime Museum** of Mykonos next door (*open Easter–Oct daily 10.30–1 & 7–9.30*), which is remarkable for its collection of **models of ships and ship designs**, from the ancient rafts of Mesopotamia to the early steamship. There are several very interesting reconstructions: a Bronze Age Theran ship, depicted in the frescoes from Akrotiri, complete with its captain's palanquin; a Greek trireme—the most concentrated naval war-machine of antiquity; an 18th century felucca. A variety of archaeological finds relating to the sea are on display—grave *stelai* of shipwrecked mariners, and even a reconstruction of an Early Roman bilge-pump. The original lantern of the Armenistis Lighthouse (1890) from northwest Mykonos—

the largest of its time in the Aegean—is exhibited in the garden outside.

Aghia Anna and the Archaeological Museum

At the eastern end of the promenade is the small *plateia*, (now the main taxi rank) named after **Mando Mavrogenous** (1796–1840), whose bust stands at its centre. Visitors in different periods have commented on how the women of Mykonos frequently appeared to outnumber men by as much as four to one, and how they were a force to be reckoned with. Mando Mavrogenous is perhaps the best known example of the courageous Mykoniot woman.

Born in Trieste to a family of prominent merchants and administrators from Ottoman Mykonos, she received a remarkable and cosmopolitan education. Returning to Greece in 1809 she became deeply committed to the cause of Greek Independence and dedicated her energy and her personal wealth to its support. Like Laskarina Bouboulina, she participated in battle action, and in 1822 led the successful repulse of a Turkish attack on Mykonos. She was instrumental in sensitising women in other European countries to the Greek Independence struggle, enlisting their moral and material help. She died, impoverished in Paros, but in the free Greece for which she had fought.

North from the square towards the ferry port (now referred to as the 'old port'), the street skirts the sandy beach of Aghia Anna: on the rise at its northern end, beside the road to the port is the **Mykonos Archaeological Museum** (*open daily except Mon 8.30–3*). The structure was built in 1905 specifically to house the finds from the 'purification *bothros*' on the island of Rhéneia. In 426 BC, following instructions of the Delphic Oracle, the island of Delos was purified for a second time (*see Delos, below*): all the bones and grave-offerings on the island were exhumed, transported to the shore of the opposite island of Rhéneia (sometimes called 'Greater Delos'), and buried in a new *bothros*, or sacred pit, which covered an area of nearly 500sq m. This was then excavated in 1898–1900, and yielded a uniquely complete range of ancient pottery stretching from the 9th century BC to 426 BC, which has been of great assistance in the identification of dates, styles and workshops of pottery from those periods. Other objects from these and from later graves on Rhéneia are exhibited, together with some statuary.

The museum's most prominent exhibit is not from Rhéneia, but was found in the Chora of Mykonos: directly ahead in the *Central Room (V)*, is the magnificent, 140cm high, 7th century BC **funerary urn**, or **pithamphora*, whose colour of clay, design of handles and figurative style is so similar to those from Xoburgo on Tinos, that this, too, must have been made by Tiniot artesans, working around 675 BC. It may possibly have been used for a child of noble birth. The fine **relief decoration** is only on one side and does not extend to the rear: around the neck is a wheeled, Trojan Horse, with the carefully depicted soldiers inside, visible through 'windows'. The lower registers, around the belly, return again and again in their figurative content to scenes of Greek warriors wresting young children from resisting and imploring Trojan women. The repeated insistence on such a scene is puzzling.

The **vase collection**, which occupies the rest of the central room and the two rooms to either side of the vestibule, is of extraordinary richness and variety. To the *right (Room II)* is shown the earlier, paler, less polished but more vigorously decorated, Geometric pottery: amongst them, the noblest in execution are the **vases from Naxos**; to *left (Room III)* are the later, much more polished, narrative scenes of the red and black figure vases of the 5th and 4th centuries BC. The sophisticated elegance of the world of 5th century BC Attica is wonderfully evoked in the *nuptial *lebes* of the Syriskos Painter**, with its exquisitely depicted dancing figures.

The two rooms at either extremity contain various objects from later burials found on Rhéneia, which after 425 BC became the official cemetery for Delos: the *room to far right (Room I)* contains a miscellaneous collection of funerary offerings—farm implements, figurines, jewellery, ornaments and perfume jars. Interesting are the contents of the **grave of Philo**, priestess of Isis on Delos, which include her ring engraved with her name, her ceremonial sistrum and some fine objects in clear glass. The centerpiece of the room is the beautiful, 18cm high, solid-cast **bronze *kouros* figure**, which was originally

the handle of a cup. The *room to far left (Room IV)* contains grave *stelai*, two of which, figuring disconsolate mariners seated on the rocks with their boats drawn up in front of them, commemorated sailors lost at sea. Note also the carefully shaped block of marble (*beside door to courtyard*), with two pairs of **footimprints** cut into its surface, perhaps of a father and son: this was a not uncommon form of votive dedication made before or after undertaking a long journey.

In the entrance vestibule is a polished Roman copy of a late Classical figure, depicting a (rather un-Herculean) **Hercules with club** and lion pelt.

AROUND THE ISLAND

(*Chora = 0.0km for distances in text*)

NORTH (CAPE ARMENISTIS) AND EAST (FTELIA, PALAIOKASTRO, ANO MERA AND KALAFÁTI)

North from the 'Old' Ferry Port, the main road follows the shoreline and passes the New Port and marina at Tourlos and continues to the sheltered, sandy beach of Aghios Stephanos. From Tourlos a steep road rises into the interior and runs north along a rocky plateau, with good views to Tinos, as far as the solitary **Armenistis Lighthouse** (5.5km), built in 1890—as if on the prow of a ship heading directly into the winds which Aeolos hurls from his alleged abode on Mount Tsikniás, across the water ahead. A kilometre and a half before the lighthouse, the road passes the **hill of Vorná**, where remains of early houses and of a fortification have been identified. The hillside shows a phenomenon found elsewhere on Mykonos in which man-made walls of large stones and boulders interlace with strange natural rock shapes to create enclosures, in a natural synergy. Over the ridge which protects Chora to the east, visible beside the road to Pánormos, is the **monastery of Aghios Panteleimon** (3km) at Maráthi, founded in 1665 (*currently closed: only open on the feast day, 27 July*). Similar to a Naxiot 'pyrgos', this is a compact, fortified quadrangle, with a dovecot incorporated in its upper west wall. The interior of the *catholicon* is decorated with 17th century wall paintings by a certain Michalis Kagianis.

The north coast of Mykonos is deeply indented by Pánormos Bay. In the middle of the wide sweep of sands at the southern extremity of the bay, a low ridge marks the site of the earliest (Neolithic) settlement on the island dating from the 5th millennium BC, at **Fteliá** (6km). The foundations of houses, excavated since the 1980s, are visible. The excavations brought to light two Late Neolithic clay figurines, household items and evidence of food from domestic hearths which suggests a very different ecology in prehistoric Mykonos—an island that was probably forested, and rich in flora and fauna. A tumulus excavated in the same area is thought to correspond with the tradition that Ajax ('the Lesser') of Locris, was shipwrecked on Gyaros after the Trojan War and drowned by Poseidon for his blasphemy against the gods (*Odyssey* IV, 499–511): his body was then buried here on Mykonos. Although often paired as a redoubtable fighter with his namesake (Ajax, son of Telamon), his roughness and rudeness earned him the hatred of Athena. He dragged Cassandra from the statue of Athena in an attempt to rape her. Thereafter the Locrians used to send two virgins each year to serve in the temple of Athena at Troy in expiation of the crime.

On a conical hill overlooking Fteliá and Panormos Bay from the east, is **Palaiokastro** (7.5km). From a distance the enceinte of mediaeval walls at the crown of the hill can be seen, with the church of Aghia Triada at the summit. The walls are considerably ruined and are built over a Byzantine fort, which in turn is built on an older ancient enceinte. This is best seen on the northwest side overlooking the bay. The central well (now filled) can still be seen. The 6th century BC explorer, Scylax of Caryanda, refers to Mykonos as '*dipolis*', i.e. possessing two cities, and it is presumed that this would have been the acropolis of the island's second city in antiquity, possibly named *Panormos*. In 1207 Mykonos was taken by the Venetians, Andrea and Geremia Ghisi, who were lords also of Tinos and the Sporades. The mediaeval remains here are from their subsequent fortress on the site. Below to the southeast are the ruins of mediaeval buildings, with a small chapel containing meagre remains of wall-paintings in the east end and apse. One of the ruined buildings encloses the foundations of an apsidal, single-aisle church dating probably from the 13th century.

To the south of the hill is the 18th century convent of the Panaghia Palaiokastrou, built tightly around an intimate courtyard, and with a carved wooden iconostasis. The screen must be contemporary with the much finer and more elaborate example in the **Tourlianí Monastery** in Ano Merá (7.5km). An inscription over the 'Royal Doors' of the **screen** in the Tourlianí dates the intricate wood-carving and painting to 1776. The gilding and delicate colour are well preserved, not diminishing the effect of the icons, whilst enhancing the finely wrought figures of the Evangelists in the architrave above; note, in particular, St John the Evangelist with the All-seeing Eye of the Almighty. The monastery—whose name refers to its '*tourlos*', or dome—was founded by monks from Paros in 1542; it was sacked by pirates in 1612, and then rebuilt in its present from in 1767. The marble cladding of the belfry is elaborately carved in a 'folk-Byzantine' style, popular in the early part of the last century: it is the work of marble-cutters from Tinos in the 1930s. For Mykoniots, the Tourlianí is perhaps the most important religious focus on the island: on feast days and Sundays it is always crowded with locals, dressed for the occasion.

Ano Merá lies in one of the few areas of relative fertility on the island, and must always have been an important inland refuge of the population during the periods of piracy. Today it is a somewhat dispersed market-village with a welcome air of normality. Beyond the village the landscape opens out into wide and spacious views: roads lead *east* into one of the few untouched, but barren, corners of Mykonos and up to the panoramic summit of **Mount Prophítis Elías Anomerítis** (341m); another road leads *southeast* to Kalafáti (11km) where, on the eastern promontory of the tongue of land which constitutes Tarsanás Point, surface excavations have revealed the presence of another Late Neolithic settlement. From Kalafáti it is possible to make excursions to the see the caves and striking rock formations of the islet of Dragonisi, just off the eastern extremity of Mykonos.

SOUTH (ANGELIKA AND LINO)

In 1991, the largest **Mycenaean tholos tomb** in the Cyclades was found on the hill of Angeliká about 1.5km south of Chora. (*120m after the Ornós junction of the ring-road round Chora, on the crown of the hill to right (west). Access is through the Hotel Tharroe of Mykonos, with their permission.*) The corbelled dome of the circular chamber rises directly from the ground, i.e. the 'dome' does not stand on a cylinder. It has an impressive diameter of c 5.5m, and is entered by a 1.8m wide *dromos*, spanned by a single lintel block. The *dromos* is curiously oriented to the south, rather than the (more customary) east. The floor of the chamber where the body was placed is cut down as if with the rectangular continuation of the *dromos*, creating a raised stone socle around. An exquisite necklace with papyrus flowers and shells in solid gold, three rock-crystal seal-stones, and a quantity of painted pottery were found in the grave, suggesting that it was the burial for someone of considerable importance. The tomb is dated to the later part of the 15th century BC.

Two Hellenistic constructions of particular interest lie close to one another a little further south on the southern slopes of the island. The first is the **Hellenistic 'tower'** at Portes which marks the hill above Platýs Gialós, and whose lintel is visible against the skyline to the east as the road descends to the beach (*reached by taking the narrow concrete road east at the summit, just before the main road makes its final descent*). Three monolithic granite blocks form the standing doorway, with the holes for the door fixtures visible. The overall dimensions are unusually small for a Hellenistic tower, however: the diameter is less than 4m. An altogether grander construction is to be seen on the hill of **Linó**, 300m to the east. (*1.2km south of the junction of the Aghia Anna road with the Airport road. Shortly after a sharp, double-turn in the road, the base of* *the tower stands ahead—well camouflaged amongst the natural boulders—on a rocky eminence to the west of the road.*) This is the base of a beautifully constructed, circular **Hellenistic tower** of the early 4th century, 11m in diameter and made of massive granite blocks, perfectly cut and interlocked. To the south are the remains of a rectangular structure of the same period, with the blocks once again cut so as to fit snugly against the natural outcrops of rock. A complex of buildings such as this would suggest that it may have been a small garrison-post with barracks, although visibility would have been limited for its use as a watchtower.

Perhaps limited visibility was no bad thing: the south coast of Mykonos is indented with the series of beautiful **sandy coves** which have made it famous, several of which are, by tradition, nude beaches. The bays are framed by the same oddly sculpted rocks and boulders as those out of which the ancient towers in the hinterland behind seem to grow. Looking at the landscape, it is easy to comprehend the origins of the legend that ascribes the formation of the island of Mykonos to the heap of projectiles and boulders hurled by Hercules and the Olympian gods in the battle with the Giants, and under which the offspring of Gaia lie buried.

PRACTICAL INFORMATION

846 00 Mykonos: area 86sq. km; perimeter 89km; resident population 9260; max. altitude 373m. **Port Authority**: 22890 22218. **Information**: Sea and Sky Travel Agency, T. 22890 28240 & 27799, fax 28287; www.mykonos.gr

ACCESS

By air: Olympic Air and Aegean Airlines both run three return flights daily between Athens and Mykonos, and one flight three times weekly to Thessaloniki. The craft are mostly 40-seater or smaller. The airport is 2.5km from Chora.

By boat: Mykonos is also amply served by connections from both Piraeus (on average three times daily in summer) and Rafina (between 5 and 9 times daily in summer), with frequency dropping markedly in winter. The fastest times are (an incredible) 2 hrs from Rafina and 4 hrs from Piraeus. The town now has two separate ports and, on departure, it is important to be sure which port the ferry you need is leaving from. There are typically an average of three connections daily to Syros and Paros, and two to Naxos, during the summer, with routes to Herakleion three times weekly. The daily caïques for Delos (except on Mondays) leave from the west mole of the old harbour.

LODGING

Mykonos has a staggering quantity of hotels on offer, catering for every kind of taste—except perhaps for rustic simplicity. For those who want to be in the heart of Chora, **Zorzis** is a small 'boutique hotel', open year-round (rare in Mykonos) with characterfully furnished rooms and friendly management (*T. 22890 22167, fax 24169, www.zorzishotel.com*). Opposite, and similar in style, is the French-owned **Chez Maria** (*T. 22890 27565, fax 27566*), which incorporates a restaurant below. Delightful and attentive, family management and unpretentiousness has always characterised the

Rhenia Hotel in Tourlos: it is set back on the hill above the new port away from noise, and 2km from the town centre (*T. 22890 22300, fax 23152, www.rhenia-bungalows.com*). Since the 1950s the **Leto Hotel** has provided spaciousness and full services, in its own gardens right beside the Chora and the museum: it is best patronised outside of high season during which it can become noisy at night (*T. 22890 22207, fax 24365, www.letohotel.com*). Of the luxury hotels, **Cavo Tagoo** is the longest standing and has the most interesting architecture (*T. 22890 23692, fax 24923, www.cavotagoo.gr*).

EATING

First, eating 'Greek': the only Mykoniot fish-taverna left in Chora which has maintained its simplicity is **Kounelas**, where it is still possible to enjoy good seafood in a tiny walled garden. (Just off waterfront, two alleys east of the town hall). Similarly traditional Greek fare and environment can be found at **To Koutouki tou Limniou** in Aghios Stephanos, north of Chora. Some of the island's best fresh fish is prepared by **Markos**' taverna at Livounia, on the east side of the Kalafáti peninsula in the east of the island. International cuisine: for imaginative Japanese and Pacific 'fusion cuisine', **Nobu** of Mykonos at the **Belvedere Hotel** in Rohari is highly prized. **Casa di Giorgio** (behind the Catholic Cathedral) has a wide variety of genuine Italian dishes prepared in an Italian kitchen. For a pleasing vantage point from which to watch the sun set, it is hard to do better than the balcony of the Veranda Bar in 'Little Venice'.

FURTHER READING

Theodore Bent's description of the 'μοιρολογίσται' of Mykonos (the versifying professional mourners at funerals), as well as being an invaluable piece of anthropological documentation, is one of the best chapters of his work *The Cyclades, or Life among the Insular Greeks (1885)*, reissued 2002 by Archaeopress, Oxford.

DELOS

Apollo and Artemis, twin siblings, were born under a palm-tree on Delos. One of the peculiarities of the Greek pantheon of gods is an unexpected specificity about their origin or place of birth: Hera born beside the Imbrasos River on Samos, Aphrodite in the waters off Kythera, Hermes on Mount Kyllene in Arcadia, and Zeus whose infancy was passed on Mt. Dikte in Crete. It is part of their innate humanity that they should have a life-story thus rooted in particularity. Much of this information is due to the creative richness of the collection of 6th century BC anonymous poems known as the '*Homeric*' *Hymns*. Although Homer himself had earlier referred in passing to the altar of Apollo on Delos in the *Odyssey* (VI. 162), the story of the god's birth on the insignificant islet of Delos is first told in detail in the *Hymn to Apollo*: in it the poet stresses—and the island itself apologises for—its barren rocks and utter poverty, seemingly so inappropriate to the home of the most resplendent of the Greek deities. But the divine association which followed had the effect of supercharging this tiny granitic, outcrop in the sea into the most sacred place in the ancient Aegean—the sea's political centre in the aftermath of the Persian wars, its commercial hub for many centuries, and consequently one of the most important archaeological areas in the Greek Islands today.

Why minuscule Delos, of all places, for such a momentous birth? Perhaps it was because of its being 'unclaimed' territory, in the very middle of things. Delos was closely surrounded by grand and powerful islands—Naxos, Paros, Kea, Tenos, Euboea—and from the beginning Delos may have appealed as a kind of neutral territory in the midst of these powers, midway between the east and west coasts of the Aegean, in which the Ionian peoples could meet for their communal festival in a place that was specifically not one of those larger islands—rather as the valley of the Forum in Rome served as neutral space for meetings of the early, hill-top tribes surrounding it. Thucydides (III. 104) comments that Pan-Ionian athletic gatherings and poetic contests were from earliest times held on Delos.

Though minute and now treeless, Delos was once well-endowed with fresh water which remained trapped above the lower layers of granite and was accessible through shallow wells. For the sacred palms mentioned by Odysseus to have grown freely on the island there must undoubtedly once have been much more surface water and vegetation. The island's harbours were also protected from the winds by the neighbouring islet of Rhéneia and by the configuration of reefs in the channel between Rhéneia and Delos. Most of all, though, the island's central position at the crossing of east–west and north–south routes through the Aegean destined it early on to a considerable degree of relevance. The establishing of a cult of Apollo, as early as the 9th century BC, subsequently reinforced by the attentions of two powerful leaders of the 6th century BC, Peisistratus, tyrant of Athens, and Polycrates of Samos, soon brought Delos preeminent fame and wealth. It also brought it grief. As the Aegean powers throughout later history sought to dominate the island and its cult for their own political ends, the people of Delos were repeatedly moved, exiled, repopulated or captured like pawns in a wider strategic power-game. The island knew immense wealth at times—latterly as a Hellenic-wide centre of commerce in slaves—and at other times, destitution and destruction at the hands of political expediency. That so much remains today after repeated sackings is somewhat of a miracle. The site is immense. Not many of the public and sacred buildings stand above their lowest courses, especially in and around the heart of the sanctuary; but on the slopes of Mount Kynthos are some of the best preserved houses from the ancient Greek world, decorated with fine mosaics and painting; there is a museum containing finds of astonishing quality; and, from the island's happiest age, are the magnificent Archaic remains—sacred buildings, the Terrace of the Lions, and the fragments of the colossal *kouros* statue of Apollo, dedicated by the people of Naxos.

Nowhere else in the Greek world have the remains of a whole city and a sanctuary of such wide-ranging importance been preserved undisturbed by modern building. Delos is a grand and instructive site, though ultimately melancholy because of the extent of its ruination and despoliation. Early morning in spring is the best moment to visit: the air is cool and full of larks, and the whole island is a meadow of wild and colourful flowers.

HISTORY OF THE ISLAND AND ITS FESTIVALS

Early history and geography

In common with a number of other places in the Greek world, Delos was also called *Ortygia*, or 'Quail Island', in remote Antiquity. Later ancient writers created a play (based on a specious etymology) on the name '*Delos*', suggesting that the island was formerly '*a-delos*' ('invisible') until the birth of the resplendent Apollo made it 'delos' ('visible'). The island is only c. 5km long by c. 1.3km wide, and is formed of granite and gneiss. The landscape is eroded and treeless: the only seasonal torrent is the ancient Inopos which drains the plain to the north of Mount Kynthos into the Bay of Skardana (northwest), forming a small circular lake along the way where once the sacred grove of palm-trees grew. The island's two harbours in the middle of the west coast are protected by the two reefs, Megalo and Mikro Rhevmatiari.

The remains of a prehistoric settlement on the top of Mount Kynthos indicate that Delos was inhabited at the end of the 3rd millennium BC. The Mycenaean period saw the first organised settlement in the harbour area and the establishment of a cult of Artemis which was to continue on the same site in later times, later as the sister of the new god, Apollo. The Ionians who began to colonise the Cyclades around 950 BC brought to Delos the cult of Leto, a possibly Lycian mother-goddess in origin, who was now described as having given birth to both Artemis and Apollo on the island. Festivals called *Delia* in honour jointly of Apollo, Artemis and Leto then began to be celebrated on the island.

In the 7th century BC, Delos, under the protection of

Naxos, became the head-quarters of a league of Aegean Ionians. In this period the island was notably embellished first by Naxos—the giant *kouros* statue of Apollo and the 'Terrace of the Lions'—and later by the island of Paros. Polycrates the 6th century BC tyrant of Samos, having conquered the Cyclades, is said by Thucydides (III.104) symbolically to have attached Rhéneia to Delos with a chain and dedicated it also to Apollo.

From early on, the Athenians took advantage of their kinship with the Ionians to enter the league of which they soon became the presiding element, sending religious embassies annually to the sanctuary led by ambassadors called '*Deliastae*', and later termed '*Theoroi*'. Latterly, as the uncontested masters of its religious affairs, they ordered a ritual purification (*catharsis*) of the sanctuary on more than one occasion. The first purification (only of the area of the island which was visible from the sanctuary itself) was orderd by Peisistratos, tyrant of Athens, in 543 BC.

The 5th and 4th centuries BC, and the Greater and Lesser *Delia*

The inhabitants of Delos took refuge on Tenos at the outbreak of the Persian Wars in 490 BC; but the Persian commander Datis, who had sent his fleet to Rhéneia, left sacred Delos untouched. After the Persian defeats in 480/479 BC, the island acquired further honour and importance as the home of the Delian League, or 'First Athenian Confederacy'—the maritime league founded in 478 BC under the leadership of Athens. The League's treasury was established on the island until it was transferred to Athens in 454 BC. A new temple of Apollo was built in Athenian, Pentelic marble between the two pre-existing temples to the god. In 426/5 BC, following an outbreak of plague, the Athenians ordered a second purification of Delos on the instigation of the Delphic Oracle, this time of the whole island (Thucydides, III, 104). They exhumed all but the most sacred burials which were on Delos and transported them to Rhéneia, passing at the same time a decree that thenceforward no one should die or give birth on Delos, and that all who were near the time of either should be carried across to Rhéneia. Strabo adds that it was unlawful even to keep a dog on the island (*Geog.* X. 5. 4).

After the purification, the Athenians restored the Delian Festival which had lapsed in the course of years, and they instituted the Delian Games which were held every four years and comprised athletic sports, horse-racing,

and musical contests. As acknowledged leaders of the Delian Confederacy, the Athenians took the most prominent
part in the ceremonies. Even though the islanders and others participated in providing choruses and animals for the
sacrifices, the leader, or *Architheoros*, was always an Athenian. For the festivities, the Athenians sent the *Theoris*—a
sacred vessel believed to have been used by Theseus—every year to Delos. During its absence, the city of Athens was
also purified and it was forbidden to execute criminals.
Before the vessel's departure, sacrifice was offered in the
Delion at Marathon in order to ensure a safe voyage. On
arrival in the island, the embassy from Athens processed
to the temple, singing the '*Prosodion*'—the hymn recount-
ing the story of Leto and the birth of the divine twins,
and intoning chants in honour of Apollo. The '*Géranos*',
or sacred 'dance of the flight of the crane', was performed
before the altar of Apollo. The *Delia* ended with theatrical
plays and banquets. The 'Lesser *Delia*' were a smaller but
annual festival.

Athens further increased her grip on the island by ac-
tively settling it with her own citizens, and in 422 BC she
banished the remaining Delians on the pretext that they
were impure and unworthy of the sacred island. She al-

lowed them to return later at the bidding of the Delphic Oracle. Athenian overseers, called *Amphictiones*, administered the temple with the nominal concurrence of the Delians. An interesting account by Plutarch (*Nikias*, 3) tells how in 417 BC Nikias, at the head of an Athenian embassy, disembarked in Rhéneia and crossed to Delos in procession on a temporary bridge of wooden barges that he had constructed. He brought with him and dedicated beside the Temple of Apollo a life-size, bronze palm-tree. The tree later fell over and in the process toppled the giant marble *kouros* statue of Apollo which had been erected by Naxos over a century and half earlier.

Delos tried repeatedly to shake off Athenian control. First, after the defeat of Athens at Aegospotami in 404 BC, the island appealed to Sparta and, from 401 to 394 BC, enjoyed a short period of independence. But Athens soon regained possession of the island and in 378 BC instituted the 'Second Athenian Confederacy', substantially different from the first Confederacy in that it was purely defensive and not an instrument of imperialism, as the latter had ultimately become. Only two years later the Athenians again had to reassert their authority when the Delians attempted to regain control of the sanctuary for the second time.

Hellenistic and Roman Delos

The Hellenistic era brought a fundamental shift in the island's character, as its commercial significance became almost as great as—if not greater than—its religious importance. On the strength of this, it entered the most prosperous and cosmopolitan period of its history, now with substantial resident communities of Egyptians, Syrians, Phoenicians, Palestinians and Jews. Rich offerings continued to flow into the sanctuary, and the number of honours decreed to foreign benefactors underlines the variety and importance of the island's diplomatic and commercial relations. The contemporary inscriptions that have survived give a detailed picture of the temple's administration and of the island's consititution. Delos was a democracy with an *archon*, a senate and an assembly. The care of the sanctuary was in the hands of four annually elected *hieropoioi*, who combined the offices of priest and administrator. A significant development for the island was the arrival of the first Roman settlers on Delos around 250 BC. It did not take long for the Roman merchants to predominate over other foreign communities. As a calculated correction to the commercial power and dominace of the island of Rhodes, which had irked Rome by its ambiguous behaviour in the Third Macedonian War, the Roman senate allowed the Athenians to reoccupy the island in 166 BC and made Delos into a tax-free port. This gave the island a crucial competitive edge. In the process, the Delians were expelled from their home yet again and the island became a clerurchy under the control of an Athenian *Epimeletes* (manager), even though the Romans still remained the true masters of the island and its trade. Strabo (*Geog.* X. 5, 4) points out that, after the razing of Corinth by Rome in 146 BC following a diplomatic incident, the merchants of Corinth moved to Delos and 'were attracted both by the immunity which the snactuary afforded, and by the convenient situation of its harbour' right at the hub of the Aegean trade routes. He adds that the religious festival had by now become a commercial affair dominated by the Romans. It was under Roman control that Delos was to become the slave-market of Greece, with as many as 10,000 slaves changing hands in a single day. As commercial gain replaced religious importance the urban landscape of the town was also transformed by the grand buildings and market-places constructed by the various guilds of foreign merchants. Italian merchants, with the backing of Rome, formed an association under the title of '*Hermaists*', and commercial syndicates of merchants from Tyre, Beirut, Alexandria, and elsewhere formed similar trade associations. The fine houses of a prosperous, mercantile bourgeoisie multiplied in the area to the southeast of the harbour.

Decline and destruction

After the island was comprehensively sacked in 88 BC by Archelaus, the general of Mithridates VI, Delos was never again to recover her former greatness—even though it was retaken for Rome the following year by Sulla, partially rebuilt with Roman aid and put once again under Athenian control. In 69 BC the island was again sacked by pirates. This led to the building of a wall round the city by the Roman legate, Triarius, to protect it from further attacks. Delos had by now become a by-word for conspicuous decline in Roman literature. In the 2nd century AD Pausanias observed that the island would remain virtually uninhabited if the temple guard were withdrawn. Philostratus (3rd century AD) even claims that the Athenians put the island up for sale and that there were no offers. The grand structures of Delos were used as a quarry for ready-cut building material by the Venetians, the Turks, and even the inhabitants of Mykonos and Tinos.

In 1445 the Italian antiquarian, Cyriac of Ancona, visited the island and was particularly impressed by the colossal Naxian *kouros* of Apollo. Under the Turks, who took Delos in 1566, the island—now named 'Sdili'—was largely abandoned. In the 17th century Sir Kenelm Digby removed marbles from the sanctuary for the collection of Charles I of England. The first excavations by French and Greek archaeologists date from as early as 1873 and have continued with only occasional interruption until the present day.

THE ARCHAEOLOGICAL AREA

(*Open daily 9–3, except Mon & public holidays. The return boat fare does not include admission to the site.*)

Already from the arriving boat the ruins can be seen stretching over a considerable area along the shore and up the hill behind. The shuttle-boats moor on a new mole constructed in what was the middle of the ancient harbour. The extension of the line of this mole eastwards roughly divides the site in two—the sacred centre of the Sanctuary on the left side, and the residential and commercial area to the right-hand side. In early times, when the religious nature of the site prevailed, the centre of activity was the former; while, during the later ascendancy of the commercial importance of the island, the rising slopes to the right became a new focus of much of the island's activities.

- Visible to the *left* is the area where the original temples of Apollo and Artemis stood at the heart of a large sacred court, surrounded by other sacred buildings and temples of other divinities, just inland of the mole. The sacred lake, where the palm-trees associated with Apollo's birth grew, overlooked by the Terrace of the Lions, stretches further to the north. On the periphery of this main area and over towards the opposite shore of the island were later Hellenistic residential and recreational areas.

- Visible to the *right* are the residential and commercial buildings, mostly dating from the Hellenistic Age and after, which are the best preserved structures on Delos, rising up the slopes of the hill towards the city's grand theatre which is visible above and to the right. Beyond this was a newer area given over to the communities of foreign merchants and to the temples of the cults they brought with them. Behind and yet further to the east rises the summit of Mount Kynthos (112m), reached by a cut stone stairway. Here have been found the earliest, prehistoric remains on Delos.

The extent of the site is considerable and several visits to the island are necessary to understand it adequately. A combination of the degree of ruination, the superimposition of different layers of different periods and the often mystifying names used means that patience is needed to unravel the complexity of what confronts the visitor.

On a visit at any time of year it is possible frequently to glimpse the island's *agama-*, or 'dragon-', lizards (*Laudakia stellio*)—similar to small iguanas—which here grow to considerable size. Often it is the characteristic head-bobbing movements of the male which reveal their presence. They were probably brought to Delos from Africa in connection with the cult of Apollo—hence the frequently encountered sculptural image of the deity as 'Apollo *Sauroctonos*', or 'lizard-slayer'.

The description of the area has been divided as follows:
- the area in and around the **Sanctuary of Apollo**;
- the **Terrace of the Lions**, the **Sacred Lake** and beyond;
- the **Museum** (where refreshments and rest may also be had);
- the **Commercial and Theatre Quarter**;
- the area of the **Terrace of the Foreign Divinities**, **Mount Kynthos** and the **Valley of the Inopos**
- **south of the harbour**.

The first three describe a consecutive loop to the north; fourth and fifth a loop to the south east; and the last is a short detour to the south.

DRAMATIS PERSONAE: THE MYTH IN BRIEF

Zeus conceived an extra-marital passion for the beautiful Leto, daughter of the Titans, Coeus and Phoebe. Zeus's rightful wife, Hera, being fearful that Leto would bear Zeus a son who would supersede Ares, her own son, in his affections, forbad every place in the world to give Leto shelter. As her time came, Leto wandered the world seeking where to give birth, but nowhere wished to incur the wrath of Hera—with the single exception of a barren, insignificant, floating island called Ortygia. The island figured it had little to lose in any case and accepted Leto willingly on condition that her children did not forswear the island because of its poverty, but would make it thenceforth one of their favourite abodes. Leto's birth pains lasted a full nine days: Hera had deliberately detained Eileithya, the divine midwife, on Mount Olympos. Eventually, by promising her a sumptuous gift, Iris persuaded Eileithya to attend, and Leto, clinging to a palm-tree, was delivered of the twins, first Artemis and then Apollo. In some accounts, Artemis even helped her mother give birth to her twin brother. The floating island was thereafter fixed to the sea-bed and became 'Delos', suffused with light and carpeted with woodland flowers (*Hymn to Apollo*, 139).

The hunting bow was the sacred symbol of both Artemis and Apollo, and the lyre also for Apollo. A high-arching haughtiness bordering on ruthlessness, characterises them both; neither had much time for pity or sympathetic sentimentality. They embodied different aspects, male and female, of purity and clarity, of cool and incisive action. The cerebral is uppermost in their worlds—a pursuit of chastity for Artemis, and of prophecy and music and art for Apollo. They represent luminousness: Artemis, the moon's crystalline light; Apollo, the sun's fearful brilliance—as well as the far-seeing, brilliance of the Greek mind in its intellectual heyday of the 6th and 5th centuries BC.

IN AND AROUND THE SANCTUARY OF APOLLO

The Harbour area

The ancient **Sacred Harbour**, where visitors and pilgrims arrived in antiquity, lies to the north of the disembarkation mole and the former Commercial Harbour to its south. Both have filled with sand and no longer possess their original outline. They were protected by a breakwater of granite blocks, 160m long, built in Archaic times, most of whose remains are now underwater. The modern mole, made of debris removed during the excavations, projects into the water between the two. The **Commercial Harbour**, extending to the south, was divided by moles into five basins. Some of the mooring stones are still visible.

Functioning like an entrance-vestibule for the sanctuary at the landward end of the modern mole, is an irregular open space called the **Agora of the Competaliasts** (*see below*). Its wide space was articulated by a circular shrine in its centre and (to south) a larger, square-based Doric structure, both of which were offerings of another association—the 'Hermaists'—to their patron god Hermes and his mother, Maia. The same association probably also built c. 150 BC the **Ionic *Naiskos***, or shrine on the north side of the square, in front of which stands a marble offertory box adorned with a relief of two knotted snakes on its upper face. The metal fixture for the box is still visible.

THE MERCHANT ASSOCIATIONS OF DELOS

Some of the names—'Competaliasts', 'Hermaists', 'Poseidoniasts'—which are associated with certain buildings on Delos are unusual. The names refer to what are in effect 'guilds', and they date from the arrival of foreign merchants from the Levant and from the Italian peninsular and Sicily who, though present on Delos from as far back as the 3rd century BC, settled in increasing numbers from c. 125 BC onwards. These foreigners, both citizens and freedmen as well their slaves, organised themselves in societies or groups of a combined social, religious and commercial nature under the patronage of particular divinities—Poseidon, Hermes, or the *Lares Compitales* (Roman ancestral guardian-spirits of the crossroads). Yearly officials were appointed for the societies. The buildings or agoras which bear their names, were constructed either with communal funds or occasionally with the specific benefaction of a member, and they represent the last developments in the city's urban design. They constitute an entirely new kind of civic focus, and are often constructed over the site of earlier buildings of a different nature.

The Sacred Way

Ignoring for the moment the wide avenue (to the left of the *naiskos*) which heads north, we follow the **Sacred Way** from the northeast corner of the paved area, whose course is still lined with *exedrae* and statue-bases between two colonnaded porticos. These porticos, which probably housed shops and stalls, provided shade and respite from heat, rain or wind. They furnished a grand approach to the sacred area, and above all glorified the power of the dynasties who built them. To the seaward side was the **Portico of Philip V** of Macedon, who was master of the Cyclades until his defeat at the hands of the Romans in 197 BC. His dedicatory inscription to Apollo in vast letters on the architrave (now resting on the ground) has survived: below is a frieze of triglyphs, while above is the cornice with rows of water spouts in the form of lions' mouths. The thickness of the building was doubled some thirty years later by the addition of another (slightly longer) *stoa* that faced the sea. On the outer face of the south end of the portico is a marble *stele*, inscribed with a 3rd century inscription regulating the sale of wood and carbon. To its right there is a curious, mediaeval graffito in Arabic.

Detour to right. To the opposite (east) side of the Sacred Way
is the **South *Stoa***, built in the 3rd century BC by the kings of
Pergamon. In front of its southern end once stood the eques-
trian statue of Epigenes of Teos, general of Attalos I of Pergamon (241–197 BC): its inscribed base survives. A narrow passage led through the middle of this portico into a wide court,
known as the **Agora of the Delians** which lies immediately
to its east. It is another irregular, paved space, once bounded
to north and east by porticos; originally there was a second
storey with Ionic pilasters—accommodating the offices of
the market. The south side is formed by an earlier portico of
the 3rd century BC standing at a slightly oblique angle. The
pattern of irregular stone foundations are from Imperial
times when Roman baths were installed here. Stretching to
the south and east are the ruins of houses; while beyond the
southeast corner of the agora, at a higher level, are the ruins
of the 5th century, apsidal **Basilica of Aghios Kirykos**. This
is one of the few Christian survivals on Delos: others were
lost in the earliest excavations. Two steps of the *synthronon*
and fragments of the *ambo* and *templon* remain. In the open
triangular area between the agora and the basilica are the remains of the circular **Shrine of Tritopator**, mythical ances-
tor of the Attic family of Pyrrhakides. (*End of detour.*)

The two parallel porticos framing the Sacred Way, formed a grand passage leading into the sacred area. Monumental **Propylaia** were constructed by the Athenians in the mid 2nd century BC at its north end to mark the entrance proper; their base is clearly visible today from the three-stepped platform in blue-gray Tenos marble on which the Doric structure in white marble stood. It had four columns defining three gateways. It appears to have replaced at least two successive, earlier *propylaia*. In front, immediately to the right, stands the eroded figure of Hermes *Propylaios*, guardian of the entrance, dedicated in 341 BC.

The Sacred Precinct

In its ruined state, it is hard at first to pick out the overall form of the *Sacred Precinct which lies ahead of you at this point. It is a large area of temples, altars, votive offerings, and remains from a thousand years of worship. It has grown up in piecemeal fashion, without overall design, around the earliest focus of cult: its development tells something of the story of the political vicissitudes of the sanctuary. The two oldest buildings are immediately to your right on entering: the **Oikos of the Naxians**, a 6th century BC building with a central axis of columns; and, about 6m to its east, the smaller and even older structure, known as Building 'Γ' (now little more than a small rectangular depression in the ground), dating from the 8th century BC. (Some scholars have suggested an earlier, Mycenaean date for the building.) Together these represent the earliest, constructed places of the cult of Apollo on Delos.

The **Oikos** ('House') of the Naxians which we see today, oriented on an east/west axis, replaced, in the early 6th century BC, a building on the same spot completed some 50 years before, which had been constructed from granite blocks with a flat, tiled roof supported on two rows of wooden columns. This first building appears to have been a temple—perhaps the earliest on Delos—to Apollo. Around 575 BC this first temple was modified: a single axial row of very slender marble columns, almost 4.50m high, now supported long marble cross-beams, which were in turn the base for a pitched roof also tiled in marble. This was groundbreaking in as much as a roof of marble had not been attempted before, and was a bold piece of engineering— especially in an area of the world so prone to seismic movement. At the same time a tetrastyle porch was added to the east. This structure was eventually superseded by other temples to the god on the site and was latterly 'redefined', or downgraded, as an *oikos* or 'house'— implying a functional use for storing sacred offerings and gifts, or as a ritual meeting place for the Naxians who had originally dedicated it—rather than specifically a place of cult. It may take its orientation from the angle of the axis of the Geometric age structure, Building 'Γ'—possibly also a temple—whose position and importance was respected throughout antiquity.

Against the north wall of the *Oikos*, stood the **colossal Statue of Apollo**, approximately four times life-size, carved from Naxian marble around the turn of the 7th century BC. The massive base though broken is still *in situ*, measuring 515 x 347 x 82cm. In its upper surface was lodged the plinth of the monolithic statue, whose principal remaining parts are now scattered a short distance to the northwest—abandoned during a failed attempt by the Venetians in the 17th century to carry them down to the port for loading onto boats. The statue must have been the largest piece of monumental sculpture in Greece at the time: it was half as big again as the giant *kouros* of Samos, which in turn was already more than twice the size of the majority of the other known marble *kouroi* from this period. The upper surface of the plinth is covered in 18th and 19th century graffiti; the Archaic dedicatory inscription is on the east face (*see below*).

Detour to see the remains of the Colossal Statue of Apollo. At a distance of c. 50m northwest, in the precinct of the Artemision (*see below*), you come first upon the **trunk** and the top of the thighs, with the row of fixture points visible for the metal belt which the (otherwise nude) figure wore; some 3m beyond, visible standing up above the mass of foundations, is the **torso**, with the pectorals barely defined on the front and the tips of locks of hair on the back. (One hand possibly belonging to the statue is in the Delos Museum; and part of a foot in the British Museum, London.) The giant figure, whose details would have been picked out in brilliant colour, probably carried a metal bow and arrow: the holes in the left pectoral would have been attachment points for this. Several graffiti of Venetian and 17th century travellers cover the surfaces. The two original ancient inscriptions, however, are on the **base** which sits beside the *Oikos* of the Naxians, and are as follows:

1. the eastern side of the base bears the **inscribed epigram**, written in archaic (6th century BC) letters: '*I am of the same stone, both figure and base*'—a statement at first appearance untrue, if the inscription is understood to mean 'of the same *block* of stone', since the two pieces always were clearly not a single block. If, on the other hand, it means, 'of the same *type* of stone' (i.e. Nax-

ian) the words could seem a statement of the obvious. Since the stone's provenance would have been clear to the ancients, however, this may simply have been a way of indicating the origin of the impressive work, without actually signing it with the words 'made by Naxians'.

2. this latter interpretation may in turn explain why the western face bears a much later, 4th century BC inscription in classical lettering (only partially visible) stating what was not written earlier: '*The Naxians, to Apollo*'. These words were probably added when the statue had to be repaired and re-erected after a gust of wind had blown the massive bronze palm-tree, dedicated by Nikias on behalf of the Athenians in 417 BC, onto the statue of Apollo and felled it. This incident is related by Plutarch (*Nikias*, 3). The base of Nikias's bronze palm has been found at a distance of 27m to the west of here. Perhaps it was later moved further away for safety's sake.

To the right of the Sacred Way are the remains of three important temples, close together in a line, facing west. First (south) the 'Great' Temple of Apollo; in the middle, the 'Temple of the Athenians' (sometimes called the 'House of the Seven Statues'); to the north, the '*Poros* Temple'. None, however, is particularly large in relation to

the importance of the place: and none curiously appears
to have an altar in front.

- The **'Great' Temple of Apollo**—the only peripteral, or
  fully colonnaded, temple in the sanctuary—was begun
  at the time of the foundation of the Delian Confederacy
  in 477 BC. It appears that it was never actually completed: construction stopped temporarily after the transfer
  to Athens of the treasury in 454 BC, and was not resumed
  until the 3rd century BC. Erected on a high base of granite blocks, and approached by steps of local marble, it
  was a Doric hexastyle edifice (29.8 x 13.5m) with 13
  columns at the side. The metopes were plain and the architrave was decorated with palm leaves and lion-mask
  spouts placed above each triglyph. The *naos* had both a
  pronaos and an opisthodomos.

- The middle structure—small, perfectly formed and
  made of finest (Athenian) Pentelic marble—was the
  Temple of the Athenians, the last of the three to be
  erected. It was built between 425–417 BC and probably
  inaugurated by Nikias. Fragments of the temple's exquisite corner *acroteria* are now in the museum, and give a
  tiny glimpse of the elegance with which the building had
  been conceived. It was a Doric amphi-prostyle structure

(17.5m by 11.3m) with six columns in front, just inside of which was a *prodromos*, or entrance hall, with four columns *in antis*. Inside the *naos* were the seven chryse-lephantine statues with Apollo in the centre, which gave the temple its alternative name of the 'House of the Seven'. These were displayed on a semi-circular pedestal of Eleusinian marble. The roof was pitched so as to accommodate the Archaic statue of Apollo made by the Naxian sculptors Tektaios and Angelion, which had previously been in the older, 'Poros Temple' beside it.

- The northernmost temple, dating from the 6th century BC, was the '**Poros Temple**', or '*Porinos Naos*' as it is referred to in inscriptions. Only the foundations (15.9 x 10m) in '*poros*' stone remain. Perhaps built in the age of Peisistratus and of a material similar to that used in Athens, the building may be the first visible expression of Athenian dominance at Delos. It was here that the treasure of the Delian Confederacy was originally lodged until its removal to Athens in 454 BC.

At a curiously oblique angle to the fronts of these last two temples is the base, in blue marble, of an **honorific dedication to Philetairos**, founder of the dynasty of Pergamon in the 3rd century BC, bearing a long, praising inscription. An adjacent base in white marble has a Doric frieze with rosettes and bulls-heads alternating with metopes. Opposite is another large dedication in yet another colour of marble—this time, pink.

PROBLEMS OF ORIENTATION

The three temples of Apollo pose unsolved questions. It is customary for Greek temples to face east; these three faced west. Temples nearly always are accompanied by an altar before the entrance; these have none. A plausible explanation is that they may have looked on to some important, pre-existing focus of cult which stood just to their west—an ancient altar, an image, a relic, or sacred spot—possibly the *Kératon (see p. 72)*. Neither literature nor archaeology can point to anything certain here, however: but it is worth also noting that the temple of Artemis looks east across this same area from the other side; and that the temple of Leto looks south towards the same point from the rise just to the north. In other words, the temples of the three protagonists of the Delian myth—the twin deities and their mother, Leto—although oriented on three different axes, all face in towards roughly the same area. Although visible on a plan, this configuration is difficult to follow on the ground, principally because the Hellenistic stoa which later enclosed the sanctuary of Artemis was erected across the area in the 2nd century BC.

The series of buildings arranged in a reverential arc which curves round the north side of the three temples to Apollo have generally been seen as treasuries on the analogy of similar structures at Olympia and Delphi. The earliest is the **Treasury of Karystos** (S. Euboea), built in the 6th century BC with four columns *in antis* to the south, and an axial row of columns supporting the roof in the interior. The **four remaining treasuries** (to the east) were built a century later on an analogous plan; the fourth in line may be the *Hestiatorion*, or ritual dining-hall, of the island of Kea, mentioned by Herodotus (IV, 34–5). Underneath this group of buildings have been found the remains of a Mycenaean structure which is thought to have been part of a noble residence.

The density of fallen remains in this area of the site means that it is easy to lose sight of the overall layout when following a linear itinerary. A general survey of the whole area is therefore outlined below. The viewing-point which has been chosen is the **low wall on the west side of the north end of the Sacred Way**, *beside a large (roundabout-like) circular pit. From here there is a good all round panorama, first east (towards the museum), then north in the direction of the Sacred Lake, and lastly west towards the water:*

Looking east

The furthest edge of the Sacred Precinct to the east is marked by a well-preserved ***peribolos* wall** constructed out of alternating rows of granite and gneiss blocks in the mid-3rd century BC. Beyond the wall at the extreme right-hand end (south) is the **house** of a merchant, Kerdon, with two peristyle courts; while beyond the opposite left-hand end of the *peribolos* (across from the Portico of Antigonos), the presence of Dionysos—whose spirit is the very opposite of Apollo's loftiness—is marked by a shrine in the form of a rectangular *exedra* (just in front of the museum building as viewed from here), which is decorated with outsized phallic symbols. This small **'Temple' of Dionysos** (only 7.5 x 3.2m) was built around 300 BC by a patron of theatre, named Karystios. The disposition of the various marble elements, though all belonging to the building, is not original: the southern pedestal bears several well-preserved and finely **carved reliefs**—a rooster with a neck and head in the form of an elongated phallus (probably one of the images used in Dionysiac processions), and on the side flanks, Dionysos with Maenads, and Silenus with a figure of Pan. When Apollo left the Oracle at Delphi each year at the winter solstice to winter in the land of the Hyperboreans, Dionysos temporarily took his place there. It seems that the two divinities—almost mutually complementary like Yin and Yang—worked in an unusual harmony and were never, as here, far from one another.

Some 25m closer to you, in front of the *peribolos* (and properly visible only by moving in that direction), is the long base of the so-called '**Monument of the Bulls**'—a misnomer which is derived from its decoration with bulls' heads.

It is an oblong building (69.4m long x 10.3m wide) of Hellenistic date and unusual design. The foundations, which alone survive, are in gneiss and granite. A *pronaos* at the south end led into a long gallery with a hollow floor placed over a partitioned framework and surrounded by a pavement c. 50cm above it. The building would have housed and displayed a military *trireme* dedicated to Apollo after a naval victory, probably by Demetrios Poliorcetes or his son, Antigonos Gonatas. The building can therefore be identified as the *Neorion* mentioned in inscriptions. A chamber at the

north end has a trapezoidal base, on which a sacred flame
dedicated to Pythian Apollo may have burned. The building
is comparable in date and form with the similar *Neorion* on
Samothrace.

To the south (right) in front of the 'Monument of the
Bulls' are the low remains of two public buildings—an
administrative **Prytaneion** of the mid 4th century BC,
comprising a porticoed entrance-vestibule with marble
benches against the walls, a small paved courtyard, a sacred area with an altar to Hestia in the northwest corner,
and a banquet-room and storage areas for archives in
the northeast corner. Grouped in front of the building to
the west are several **altars** of different periods, dedicated
principally to the protecting divinities of the city—Athena Polias and Zeus Polieus. To the north of the Prytaneion
is a much earlier structure (6th century BC) sometimes
identified as the Bouleuterion, or Council Chamber.

Looking north

The northern boundary of the precinct is marked by the
120m long **Portico of Antigonos Gonatas** erected in the
second half of the 3rd century BC (clearly visible on your
right if you go a few metres to the north).

The portico, with a frieze of triglyphs also decorated with bulls' heads, has two longitudinal galleries with a salient wing at either end: in the east wing a statue of the early 1st century BC Roman general, Caius Billienus, has been replaced on its base. In front of the portico are two parallel lines of pedestals on which stood some twenty statues of the ancestors, real and mythical, of Antigonos Gonatas; the idea may have been inspired by the Monument of the Eponymous Heroes in the Agora of Athens.

A couple of important Archaic sites can be seen abutting the portico to north and south. In the northeast corner just outside of the back wall of the portico is the **Fountain of Minoa**—a stepped, rectangular cistern or well which still contains water year-round—built in the mid-6th century BC and originally covered by a roof. In front of the portico in the centre is a small roughly circular burial area, identified as the '**Theke (Tomb) of Arge and Opis**' (*see below: Apollo and the Hyperboreans*). This is in effect a Mycenaean ossuary, comprising small chamber tombs reached by a *dromos*, in which were found skeletons and both Mycenaean and pre-Mycenaean vases. Arge and Opis were two of the Hyperborean maidens mentioned by Herodotus (*Hist.* IV, 35), who came to Delos at the time of the birth of Apollo and Artemis: he adds that some very particular sacrificial rites were performed at their place of burial by the women of the island.

Looking west and northwest

Looking west towards the shore of the former Sacred Harbour, the precinct is bordered by the **Stoa of the Naxians**, whose long rear wall backed onto the harbour quays. An arm of the stoa also runs east to join the main *propylaia*. This structure was a part of the 6th century BC building programme of the Naxians, which had begun with their '*Oikos*': as one of the first examples of the organisation and enclosing of space by colonnades of this nature, it was a highly innovative piece of design. In the *stoa*'s southwest corner are the granite foundations, with a cylindrical hollow in the middle, of the **base of the Bronze Palm Tree** dedicated by Nikias in 417 BC. On one of the fragments (replaced) of the lower marble course of the monument can be read the name of Nikias, beginning the dedicatory inscription.

Immediately in the foreground when looking west is the long, right-angled base of the **Ionic portico of the Artemision**, whose columns are visible standing just beyond the fragment of the colossal statue of Apollo. This defined an area occupied at its centre by three successive sacred buildings raised on top of one another. This is probably the oldest place of worship on Delos, where a female divinity—a precursor of Artemis—was honoured long before the appearance of Apollo on the scene.

At the lowest level is a **Mycenaean place of cult**. Although the obvious continuity of cult here is interesting, it would be misleading to call this a 'temple' to 'Artemis', since both these appellations bring different, more recent connotations with them. In 1946, the exquisite **ivory pieces and plaques** now exhibited in the museum were found at this lowest level. Directly on top of this, in the mid-7th century BC, an Archaic **Temple to Artemis** was raised, embellished by statues of *korai* found on the site, the most famous of which is that dedicated by Nikandra—one of the earliest pieces of Archaic sculpture known—now in the Archaeological Museum in Athens. The **last temple of Artemis** whose remains are visible today, dates from the Hellenistic period. Near its west side stand the two imposing fragments of the Colossal statue of Apollo (*see above*).

The somewhat chaotic area directly south of the Artemision contains the foundations of several ancient and important places of cult: a semicircular platform hewn in the rock, which is perhaps the '*sema*' mentioned by Herodotus where a cult, associated with the tomb of another two Hyperborean maidens, Laodice and Hyperoche (*see below*) who brought the first of the yearly offerings to Apollo, was practised. Abutting the south side of the temple of Artemis are the remains of a building often identified as the **Kératon**, a building which once housed the sacred and ancient 'altar of horns', said to have been fashioned by Apollo himself, and before which, according to legend, Theseus danced on his return from Crete together with the Athenian men whom he had saved from the Minotaur: this 'dance [resembling the flight] of the crane', or *géranos*, was ritually performed at the altar of Apollo throughout antiquity. The altar appears to have been composed of the horns of goats and other animals (many of them hunted down by his twin-sister Artemis). The existing remains are of a building of Athenian construction, dating from the middle of the 4th century bc, which enshrined the ancient altar.

APOLLO AND THE HYPERBOREANS

Grandly named yet vaguely defined, the Hyperboreans ('from beyond the North Wind') were a legendary race of Apollo-worshippers who lived in the far north of the world as imagined by the Greeks. They and their magical existence are mentioned in passing by Hesiod and by Pindar; a fragment of Alcaeus suggests that Apollo left his customary Greek abodes each year after the winter solstice and wintered in the land of the Hyperboreans. Other than the god, only heroes such as Perseus or Hercules could reach their land. By the time Herodotus wrote in the 5th century BC the arrival of the yearly offerings sent by the Hyperboreans to the sanctuary at Delos was already a long established tradition. What exactly the offerings were is unclear, but we know that they were always carefully wrapped in straw; where they ultimately came from was equally unclear, but their route— described by Herodotus (*Hist.* IV, 34–5) was precise and unchanging. The offerings came from the Hyperboreans to the Scythians, whence they were ceremonially passed between neighbouring people, until they arrived at Dodona in the mountainous northwest of Greece, whence they were passed to Euboea over the Malian Gulf; from Karystos on Euboea they were then passed to the people of Tenos, who finally delivered them to the Delians. The first maidens who made this journey to accompany the offerings were Hyperoche and Laodice; they died in Delos and are remembered here, close by the Temple of Artemis. Herodotus mentions two other maidens, Opis and Arge, who came to Delos even earlier, 'at the same time as Artemis and Apollo'. They are honoured in the circular *theke* before the south front of the portico of Antigonos Gonatas. These unusual legends, and the unusual method of the arrival of the offerings, may have represented a desire by the Delians to have a tradition akin to the *Daphnephoria* of Delphi.

The furthest area, visible to the northwest, beyond the Artemision and west of the Sacred Harbour, was in antiquity dominated by a vast (56.5 x 34.3m), closed meeting-hall. It was known as the '**Hypostyle Hall**' from the 44 columns in its interior that supported its wide roof and the central lantern that admitted light from above. This unusual structure dates from the late 3rd century BC and may possibly have had both a religious use (hosting the celebrations of the festival of Poseidon in mid-winter) and a secular use (as a meeting-hall for grain-traders). To the south it looked out, from its only open side, onto the large esplanade, raised on an embankment, known as the **Agora of Theophrastos** and named from the plinth in its centre bearing an inscription to a certain Theophrastos who was *Epimelete* (a chief supervisor) in 126/5 BC. Another surviving base commemorates L. Cornelius Sulla.

THE TERRACE OF THE LIONS, THE SACRED LAKE AND BEYOND

Around the Letoön

In the northwest corner of the Precinct of Apollo are two buildings: the **Ecclesiasterion**, an assembly building first erected in the early 5th century BC and then re-modelled more than once in Hellenistic times, whose marble seats along the north wall to either side of an aedicule are still well-preserved *in situ*; and, across from it, a small rectangular edifice of the late 5th century BC, referred to generally as an **'Administrative Office' building**. Between the two, a tiny passageway latterly remained the only access in and out of the Sanctuary from the north. Continuing north, the pathway passes beside two important sacred structures. Immediately to the left is the **Sanctuary of the Twelve Gods** or *Dodekatheon*, attested here from Archaic times and dedicated probably to four triads of gods: Zeus, Hera and Athena; Apollo, Artemis and Leto; Hades, Demeter and Kore; and Poseidon, Aphrodite and Hermes. The granite base of the temple and marble elements of the superstructure at the west end are visible, and a number of the dozen altars which lay in its precinct are clustered to the east. Almost contiguous to the north, and opposite what was once a complex of shops, is the **Letoön**, constructed around 540 BC in a veined, white marble, and consecrated to the mother of Apollo and Artemis, without whose exhausting search for a place to give birth and final choice of Delos, there would never have been any sanctuary here in the first place. The temple is built over a widely protruding marble *crepis* which forms a beautifully rounded ledge in Parian marble, on which offerings were laid; it had a paved vestibule, giving access to the naos which protected the seated effigy of Leto. The temple is small, but its *temenos* appears to have stretched some considerable way to the east—an area now occupied by the large, open area of the **Agora of the Italians**. The latter was laid out in the late 2nd century BC, but never fully completed.

Detour into Agora of the Italians. The size of the agora (overall almost 100 x 70m) gives some sense of the importance and wealth which the community of Italian merchants had achieved on Delos by the 2nd century BC through banking and trade in slaves and other commodities. The area is entered through a ruined Doric Propylon. The wide, central space of beaten earth is surrounded by a Doric **peristyle of**

white marble columns on red bases (the latter visible on the north side). It formerly had an Ionic, colonnaded gallery above. The construction was donated by several individuals or trade groups known as Hermaists (*see p. 53*). Begun in c. 110 BC, it was repaired after the sack of Delos by Mithridates, but then left unfinished around 50 BC. On the inner side is a series of rooms or *exedrae* containing votive monuments, statues, and mosaics: noteworthy on the west side are those of *Lucius Orbius, Caius Cluvius,* and *Caius Ofellius* (where a fine nude statue by the Athenian sculptors Dionysios and Timarchides, now in the museum, was found); the room of *Publius Satricanius,* on the north side has a **fine mosaic**. In an *exedra* on the east side was found a statue of a *Wounded Gaul* (now in Athens). A building such as this—comparable to today's shopping malls—would have been thronged with life in the daylight hours: make-shift stalls in the central court selling goods under canopies would have been fixed to the colonnade, so that people sauntered in the shade of the colonnade itself between parallel rows of shops to one side and stalls to the other. On the outer east and west sides of the structure are more lines of shops opening into the street.

West of both the Italian Agora and of the Letoön are the remains of a **granite building** with a double court: the ground floor was divided into small rooms, perhaps sculptors' workshops (statues of an unfinished sphinx and gryphon are visible), while above may have been an assembly room.

Around the Sacred Lake

The avenue leading north from the Letoön begins to open out and is bordered to the west by the celebrated *Ter-race of the Lions, which constitutes a ceremonial entry of a kind clearly influenced by similar avenues in Egyptian sanctuaries. (The original sculptures are now in the museum; good copies have been placed on site.) This line of magnificent creatures—more panthers than lions—laid out and executed by the Naxians in their native stone some time at the end of the 7th century BC, faces the rising sun across the Sacred Lake where Apollo and Artemis were born. Their elongated backs, lean flanks and crouching haunches are charged with attentive energy. They were once the ceremonial guardians of the entry to the Sanctuary—that is, in earliest times when boats landed *not* in the Sacred Harbour (which had not yet been constructed), but in the Bay of Skardana instead, which lies over the rise to the north of here. The logic of this older entry, which first passed by the Sacred Lake with its palms and swans, and then proceeded south under the gaze of the lions towards the Temple of Leto and thence to the

Sanctuaries of Apollo and Artemis, was impeccable. The effect of later re-orienting the Sacred Precinct for arrival from a harbour to the south side was to render the Terrace of the Lions somewhat irrelevant.

> Although five lions are visible *in situ*, their original number was at least nine, and could even have been as many as 16. One, removed by the Venetians in 1716, now stands by the entrance to the Arsenal in Venice, completed with an 18th century head.
>
> The lion was traditionally more closely associated with Artemis than with Apollo for whom it had no particular significance, and it is noteworthy that the positioning of the lions here is more in alignment with the Temple of Artemis than with that of Apollo. At the time the terrace was created in the 7th century BC, the prominence of Artemis at Delos may have been much greater than it was in later times.

The lions look onto the **Sacred Lake**, now dry since 1925 when it was drained for reasons of salubrity. Its form is indicated by a modern wall, which represents its extent in Hellenistic times. This is the lake referred to as 'round like a wheel' (τροχοειδής), of which Herodotus was reminded when describing the Sacred Lake of Sais in Egypt (*Hist.* II, 170). In it were kept the sacred swans and geese of Apollo.

The lake was formed by an overflow of the Inopos torrent which originally debouched to the north, into the Bay of Skardana. A palm-tree has been planted in the centre in memory of the grove which grew here in Antiquity and of the sacred palm to which Leto clung when giving birth to the twins.

The Sacred Lake was once the first element of the Sanctuary of Apollo encountered by visitors; today it is one of the last, and it marks the northern limit of the sacred area in early Antiquity. The extensive remains that lie beyond it, on the hill of Skardana to the north, all date from Hellenistic times and after. Beyond them, the land drops steeply to the **Bay of Skardana**, which was the island's harbour and entrance up until the building and organisation of the Sacred Harbour during the course of the 6th century BC.

The Hellenistic Constructions north of the Sacred Lake

The re-erected columns visible to the northwest of the Lion Terrace belong to the large edifice of the **Association of the Poseidoniasts of Berytos** (modern Beirut), a guild of Syrian ship-owners and merchants who worshipped Baal, a god they identified with Poseidon.

The vestibule leads into a court bounded on the west by a portico onto which opened four sacred rooms. One of these, later than the others, was dedicated to the goddess Roma—a popular cult, in fashion in the late 2nd century BC—and contains her statue. On the east side a colonnade leads to a peristyle court, with a cistern. Note the clear, **dedicatory inscription** of the Poseidoniasts 'to the gods of their fathers' along the west-side entablature. Further to the west is another open court with a mosaic pavement, which was probably used as a meeting-place. To the south were reception rooms and, in the basement below them, a series of shops. A number of **statues** were found in this building including the memorable group of *Aphrodite and Pan* (now in the National Museum in Athens), in which the goddess threatens the menacing Pan with her sandal: the work is probably an original of the 3rd century BC, much influenced by Praxitelean forms.

Beyond the Building of the Poseidoniasts a road runs north/south along the side of four houses, some of which bear apotropaic symbols carved beside their doorways— a phallus, a man holding an animal, a cutlass, etc. These and other symbols, such as the club of Hercules or the conical caps worn by the Dioscorides, can be found elsewhere in the area. The clearest examples are on the two marble door-posts of the house set slightly back to the west from the middle of the street. Their symbolic purpose was to protect the dwellings from evil spirits. Note also the floors in attractive chequer-board mosaic in the houses at the south end.

To the north, along a straight east/west street, two entire blocks of houses have been excavated: their urban plan (later and more organised than their counterparts to the south in the Theatre Quarter), their functional furnishings (latrines and ample cisterns), their cool two-storey marble peristyles ('**House of the Comedians**') and their decoration with reliefs and mosaics, give a sense of the comfortable life of Hellenistic Delos. The easternmost building, known as the '**House of the *Diadumenos***', from the discovery here of a replica of the celebrated statue by Polyclitus, had an elaborate water-supply system. Many of the houses similarly take their names from the exemplary finds made in them which are now exhibited in the museum ('House of the Jewels', 'House of the Seals', etc.) The *'**House of the Lake**', which occupies a whole block on its own, has an especially well preserved peristyle of monolithic columns with a mosaic *impluvium* floor. Its northeast corner (opposite the entrance to the 'Granite Palaestra') bears a large fish/phallus image for good fortune, carved in relief on one of the granite corner-blocks.

One of Delos's most celebrated finds—a magnificent male portrait in bronze, executed with a thoughtful and sensitive naturalism, and still preserving its original eyes (now in the Archaeological Museum in Athens)—comes from the so-called '**Granite Palaestra**' (mid-2nd century BC). This massive structure lies due north of the Sacred Lake (directly beyond its older and more ruined sister-edifice, known as the 'Lake Palaestra') and takes its name from the granite blocks of which it is partly constructed: these survive well in the fine extent of the south wall. In the middle is a large cistern in four compartments, with a roof in *poros* stone, which was surrounded by a Doric peristyle. Extending both due south and northwest from the Granite Palaestra are well-conserved stretches of the **City Wall**.

The enceinte, often called the 'Wall of Triarius', was built by the Roman legate, Triarius, in 69–66 BC to protect Delos from the attacks of the pirate, Athenodoros. It was partly built over houses and shops which were demolished and filled with rubble to form a foundation. The southern stretch of the wall was removed in 1925–26. It skirted the east side of the Sacred Lake and of the Agora of the Italians. On a bastion of the wall, directly east of the Italian Agora, was found a small **Prostyle Temple** of the 2nd century BC with four columns, open to the east, and with an altar in front dedicated to a female goddess—possibly Aphrodite.

The northeast of the island

Detour to east (area not properly cleared and often closed off)
Those with the time and enthusiasm to explore further can continue to the northeast of here. The first building, after 100m, is the ancient *Archegesion*, sacred to the worship of Apollo in the person of Anios, the legendary first settler and king of Delos. The latest part of the structure dates from the 6th century BC; but inside the southeast corner, seven 7th century BC tombs were found undisturbed, having escaped removal during the second purification of Delos because of their sacred nature. A further 100m on are the remains of the square Ionic peristyle of the **Gymnasium**, and beyond it the **Stadium**; these were both built before the **Xystos** (a covered track for winter training) was added around 200 BC, to the east side of the stadium in order to join the two structures together. Beyond the stadium is a cluster of ancient houses. Near the island's eastern shore are the remains of a **Synagogue**. The building is remarkably early—dating from the mid 1st century BC—making it one of the very earliest known synagogues outside of Palestine. The Jewish community was probably already established a century earlier (cp. *I Macabees*, 15. 23).

The remains of a **murex-processing workshop,** for the production of purple dye, lies close to the shore about 800m south of the Synagogue.

THE MUSEUM

The core of the museum is a magnificent *collection of **Archaic sculpture** from the site, dating from what was arguably the island's artistic and spiritual zenith—the 7th and early 6th centuries BC—before the controlling hand of Athens made itself felt in the sanctuary and its art. These are all works from the great sculpting centres of Naxos and Paros, and they possess the clarity, purity and vigour of artists who knew and perfectly understood their medium—the soft, crystalline, local marble that came from the two islands. The pieces are mostly worked not with iron but with bronze tools, and they consequently have the simpler forms and volumes which softer tools impart. Drapery in the female statues, or *korai*, does not hide the forms of the body in Archaic sculpture, but enhances them; similarly the effect of the nakedness of the male *kouroi* is to simplify and emphasise the volumes.

The Central Hall (*Galleries I & II*) displays a fine assembly of fragmentary, **Apollonian kouroi**: some of the heads, although damaged or eroded, are of great beauty (especially the couple against the right wall). The centre of the gallery is occupied by a large **Triangular Dedication Base** with its narrow point decorated with a ram's head and the other two corners with apotropaic gorgon masks. The inscription in clear Archaic lettering on the left side states that the base carried a statue (of Apollo) by the late 7th century BC, Naxian sculptor, Euthychartides. In the immediate right-hand corner, on entering the room, is the **hand of the colossal Apollo** of the Naxians which held the bow. Towards the centre is the **Archaic Sphinx** of Parian workmanship (early 6th century BC), re-placed on its Ionic capital which would once have stood on top of a monolithic column (cp. similar sphinxes at Delphi and at Aphaia on Aegina). Just beyond is a group of fragments of several **figures of divinities**: even the small bust and shoulders of a goddess gives ample scope to observe the beautifully rhythmic patterning of their design. At the end of the hall are two **doves** from the Heraion, and (*end bay*) a pair of **lions** from the Temple of Artemis with small perforations along the spine for the affixing of a gilded, bronze mane.

The right-hand (*south*) area of *Gallery III* has a number of **fragments of**

men on horses similar in date and conception to the 'Rampin Rider' in Athens. In a room on their own further to the right are the original *****lions from the Terrace of Lions**. These sleekly stylised beasts—which differ notably from one another—show how much early Greek art was influenced by Egyptian ideas and techniques, but also how different and independent and confident its own Greek voice was becoming. Notwithstanding the toll taken by wind erosion and damage, the detail of the haunches and feet, of the elongated flanks with protruding ribs, and of the modelling of the shoulders—where it has survived—is admirable. It heralds a new attention to a raw energy which is quite different from anything in Egyptian art prior to this period.

In the left-hand (*north*) area of *Gallery III*, we are already in the Classical world—full of movement, naturalism and narrative. The stillness and vigour of the Archaic is gone, however. The centerpiece here is an elaborate tableau which was the *acroterion* **of the eastern pediment of the Temple of the Athenians** (c. 420 BC), depicting an Athenian legend in which Boreas, god of the North Wind, abducts Oreithyia, the daughter of King Erechtheus of Athens.

In *Gallery IV* (*northeast corner of building*) we come to mostly later Hellenistic statuary, where the use of the running-drill to 'undercut' the marble and create deeply folded drapery is now paramount: the drapery is fine, especially on the female statue, but seems at times to weigh the figures down—in a manner similar to female costume in 18th century Europe. It unfurls dynamically, however, in the beautiful, 4th century BC piece of **Artemis taking a Stag** in the hunt. In the attractive, archaising relief of Hermes leading Athena, Apollo and Artemis (*immediately left on entering*), some of the original colour still remains; and on the same left side of the gallery, the original (red) under-colouring persists is the sandals under the feet of the statues. The north (end) wall of the gallery shows one of the finest Delian **mosaic floors** with a sumptuous border of fruit and flora,

removed from a house on the Hill of Skardana. Its black, red and yellow colours are particularly vibrant.

Gallery V (*north side of building*) is dominated by an enormous **statue of Caius Ofellius Ferus** from the Agora of the Italians, carved around 115 BC by two Athenian sculptors, Dionysios and Timarchides, showing the extent to which Greek artists now adapted themselves wholly to a dominating Roman style. In the arch between the *Galleries VI* and VII, is a rare votive stele which has survived with its bronze plaque depicting Artemis presiding at a sacrifice (3rd century BC). In *Gallery VI*, the finest aspects of Roman art come out in the characteristically naturalistic **portrait busts**. The base pedestal for a bronze Roman statue with the broken, bronze foot still in position shows how such figures were customarily attached into marble blocks by means of lead dowels which filled the inside of the foot for greater stability, and locked the piece into the marble base below.

Gallery VII (*which returns to the main entrance*) is filled with a fascinating selection— one of the best outside the Archaeological Museum of Naples—of domestic objects and decorations, which give a rare view of the extraordinary intensity and clarity of the decorative finishings to the interiors of houses. (*West side*): votive terracotta **figurines** of great delicacy, as well as moulds for their production in series; fine marble figurines for temple offerings, and several **mosaic emblemata** with leopards, doves etc. (*East side*): **jewellery** of remarkable refinement incorporating elements in glass paste and semi-precious stones, fragments of wall-paintings, mostly of interest for their decorative detail and chromatic intensity (examples of pigments used); a showcase containing explicitly erotic and phallic objects, including a memorable relief of two **jousting, winged phalli** (once coloured), each endowed with its own phallus as well as a phallic tail, above an inscription which reads, 'this for me and this for you'. The decorative painted friezes exhibited make extensive use of a brilliant, iron-oxide red, and some of the marble statuary shows vestiges of the same colour. Many of the sketched scenes were advertisements for fights or spectacles—similar to 'posters' on the outside of buildings—and those overwritten with ancient graffiti were from public places. A show-case displays **glass and tableware**, with kitchenware (grills and frying-pans) and mixing receptacles nearby, and a **circular lamp** with 24 flames for illuminating a room. In the centre of the room is an exquisite *****table-top** in an engraved and painted, dark marble. Few other collections give a more vivid sense of the liveliness and elegance of Hellenistic interiors than this one room.

Gallery VIII (*to right of the main entrance—frequently closed*) exhibits the finds from earliest antiquity, and the museum's vase collection. Of particular note and refinement are the *****carved Mycenaean ivory tablets** of the 13th century BC (*first case in centre*), found below the Artemision, together with (*right*) a bronze statuette of a helmeted figure (?deity) holding a harp. The wide provenance of the ceramic objects—Rhodes, Chios, Melos, Corinth—reflects the vigour of Delos's early trading and presents a remarkable variety of styles and colours.

THE COMMERCIAL AND THEATRE QUARTER

Below the Theatre

In contrast to the area of the Sanctuary of Apollo, the degree of conservation of streets and dwellings in the southern sector of the city is remarkable and bears comparison at times with Pompeii. The beauty and sophistication of the houses provide a lively picture of civil and domestic life and architecture in Hellenistic Greece.

The typical **Delian house** of the Hellenistic and Roman period had its rooms grouped around a central courtyard which was reached from the street by a short corridor. In the absence of external windows, this well of light was the sole illumination of the tenebrous interiors, and served to keep the air cool during the summer months. Richer homes had a peristyle round the court, with marble columns, and the walls plastered, painted and polished to a shine, so as to maximise the light. The so-called 'Rhodian Peristyle' is also found on Delos, consisting of a large hall rising the full height and fronted by a taller colonnade occupying one side, and generally two storeys of rooms constituting the others. The central court would normally have a mosaic floor, whose brilliant colours revived when wet: this served as an *impluvium* catching rainwater for the all-important cistern beneath. Some houses possessed wells; but stored rainwater was generally preferred because of its supposed beneficial and medicinal qualities.

From the southeast corner of the Agora of the Competaliasts at the head of the embarkation mole, the **well-paved and drained main street** of the Theatre Quarter ascends between houses and shops—some furnished with marble windows for dispensing sales—giving directly on to the street. Occasional niches show that the street was lit by lamps at night. To the right is a house with a stove and built-in basins, probably a **dyer's workshop**. A small passage and steps lead (*right*) up, past a dolphin mosaic covering a cistern, into the **House of Cleopatra**. The marble colonnade has been restored; in the courtyard stand replicas of the two elegant statues (*now in the museum*) representing Cleopatra and Dioscourides, the 2nd century BC, Athenian owners. On the opposite side of the road (*left*) is the **House of Dionysos**, where part of the staircase to an upper floor remains. In one room the rough plaster has graffiti (triremes, horseman, etc.), perhaps done by the plasterers before they added the surface layer for the painted marbling. The courtyard contains a particularly elegant *mosaic of Dionysos, executed in *opus vermiculatum*, i.e with tiny *tesserae* of often varying shapes which enhance the pictorial effect; the god is seen crowned with ivy leaves and holding a *thyrsos*, mounted on a tiger wreathed in vines. The binding cement has been variously tinted with the colour of the *tesserae* it holds, so as admirably to increase the tonal unity and fluidity of the design. These mosaics must be imagined gleaming from beneath standing water rather than in their present dusty condition. Farther along, the **House of the Trident**, one of the largest houses on the island, has a 'Rhodian' peristyle and an elegant well-head. The **mosaics** are simple but striking, and include an anchor with a dolphin and a trident with a ribbon tied in a bow: the resemblance between this design and the trademarks on amphorae found in a sunken ship off Marseille has been pointed out, suggesting that the house may have belonged to the Delian wine-merchant who owned the ship. Another mosaic depicts a Panathenaic amphora suggesting that a member of the household had won a victory in a chariot-race.

The Theatre and Hellenistic houses

At the top of the first rise the street emerges into the space before the *cavea* of the **theatre**, built in the early 3rd century BC. It held around 5,500 spectators. The *cavea* also served as a large water-catchment area during rainstorms: two well-preserved drain-mouths can be seen to either side of the semi-circular *orchestra*, which conduct the water into the impressively *__vaulted cistern__ below. The stone arch is not a common element in Greek architecture: the eight granite spans here are well-preserved examples. The cistern was originally roofed with marble blocks and would probably have held around 500,000 litres of water for communal use when full.

The *cavea* is partly cut into the hill and partly built up to either side with bulwarks of fine isodomic blocks, rusticated for the most part and becoming polished closer to the sides of the stage. Only in the lowest tier are the backs of the seats preserved. The large and once elaborate *skene* was in the form of a rectangle with colonnades on all four sides—a design not found elsewhere. On the side facing the audience it would have had engaged Doric columns and was flanked by *paraskenia*, each having two higher columns. From the highest point of the theatre, 18m above the *orchestra*, there is a fine view over the excavations and the shore. Twenty metres to the south of the cistern are the large foundations which supported the Altar of Dionysos with, behind it, remains of a small Temple of Apollo, dated by an inscription to 110/109 BC. Two adjacent shrines were dedicated to Artemis-Hecate (*west*) and Dionysos, Hermes, and Pan (*east*).

Beside the theatre to the southeast, and entered through a fine **marble doorway**, is a building known as the 'Hostel'. It had three stories and a very large cistern, almost 20m deep, with a feed-pipe from the gutters visible in the southwest corner; a marble washing-slab with drainage indentation also lies near the entrance. The building is thought to have been a guesthouse which put up visitors to the Delian festivals.

The path east from the theatre towards the base of Mount Kynthos, passes between two of the best-preserved Hellenistic houses on Delos: to the right hand side, the *House of the Masks, a large, merchant's house which consists of a complex of shops, workshops and living-quarters all in the same block.

The side looking onto the street consists of shops which would have been rented out by the owner; the residence (*entered by circumventing the west side of the block*) is set back to the south, around a peristyle of fluted columns built beside a deep, rock-cut cistern, which was originally covered by a wing of the house. Well-preserved reception rooms look onto the court from the north, each with mosaic floor and painted walls, showing several layers of successive decoration (frequently painted to represent marble). The *mosaics in the central room have an abstract field surrounded by theatrical masks: in the subsidiary room to the east is a famous and technically masterful depiction of Dionysos, wearing flowing oriental garb, seated on a panther. He holds the *thyrsos* and a tambourine; the detail shows even the whiskers of the animal. (*Splashing the mosaic with water helps to enliven the colours and details properly.*) The same theme appears elsewhere in Delos, and in Hellenistic floors in both Pella and Eretria, suggesting that the mosaic workers had a popular repertoire in common, perhaps transmitted within workshops through a kind of 'pattern book'. The square fixture holes in the peristyle columns for blinds or screens are still visible at a height of about 220cm above the ground.

A similar design is found in the **House of the Dolphins**, just to the northeast, named after its magnificent central *****mosaic**.

Concentric rings of elegant wave, key, and gryphon-head designs, surround a central *emblema* which has survived only scantily: pairs of stylised dolphins, ridden by small figures with divine emblems, fill the corners. The mosaic bears a (rare) signature by the artist, a certain '[*Askle*]piades of Arados'—a town in Phoenicia. Perhaps not unconnectedly, another mosaic in the entrance-way bears an apotropaic symbol of Tanit, the Phoenician moon-goddess. Here the peristyle is formed of columns which are only fluted for half of their height: the drain from the impluvium into the cistern below is on the south side. The holes for the wooden door-imposts are clearly visible in the marble thresholds.

MOUNT KYNTHOS, 'THE TERRACE OF THE FOREIGN DIVINITIES' AND THE INOPOS VALLEY

Mount Kynthos

The horizon to the east of the House of the Dolphins is dominated by the abrupt rise of Mount Kynthos. An ancient stone path, partly stepped, leads up to the east before turning south to the summit. To the right of the pathway is a curious shrine known as the '***Antron***' or 'Cave of Hercules'. It is in the form of a grotto with an entrance (facing due west) and a pitched roof formed by ten granite slabs of very large dimensions, placed against one another in pairs, in a fashion reminiscent of the Sybil's Cave at Cumae, near Naples. The massive blocks of the boundary wall in front are beautifully engaged with the natural bedrock. Earlier visitors can be forgiven for seeing in this impressive construction a pre-Classical shrine, possibly a 'birth-place of Apollo'. The fact that nothing earlier than Hellenistic finds have been recovered here, however, has led archaeologists to suggest that this deliberately archaic method of construction was self-consciously adopted as part of a fashionable revival of the ancient, mythical worship of Hercules—a phenomenon not infrequently found in Hellenistic times. Inside, a base of reddish granite supported a Hellenistic statue of the hero, fragments of which are in the museum. This was illuminated by light from above, as if through an open '*oculus*'. In front of the entrance is the marble base of an altar, also Hellenistic. Although the appurtenances are later, the cultic use of such a natural cleft in the hillside is likely nonetheless to be far more antique than the remains that have been found.

In the corner of the first sharp turn in the stepped pathway is a sanctuary attributed by the Athenians to *Agatha Tyche* (Good Fortune), which later served as a '**Philadelpheion**', dedicated to the cult of Arsinoe, sister and wife of Ptolemy II Philadelphos, who was deified after her death in 270 BC. From here the summit of **Mount Kynthos** (112m) is easily reached; the mountain's name was used as an epithet for both Apollo and Artemis, who must have been worshipped here in the 7th century BC. The pathway passes numerous ruined monuments, aedicules and shrines.

The site has yielded remains of Cycladic dwellings of the 3rd millennium BC, but was abandoned for long periods and became an important sanctuary only in 281–267 BC when the existing buildings were rebuilt and a rectangular *peribolos* constructed. On the flattened summit stood the **Sanctuary of Kynthian Zeus and Athena**, with niches for votive offerings, statue bases, and a dedicatory mosaic. One hundred metres to the southeast, on the south summit, are the remains of a small **Sanctuary to Zeus *Hypsistos*** (the 'highest'—possibly here a Greek appellation for Baal). To the east, on a barely accessible terrace, has been excavated the 5th century BC **Sanctuary of Artemis *Locheia***, with the foundations of a temple having a doorway in the middle of the longer, south side. On the way down the north side are the ruins of over a dozen other tiny sanctuaries dedicated to unknown and oriental deities. A large, protruding rock, 100m north of the summit, bears the 5th century BC **inscription**, 'the boundary of Leto'.

The Heraion

Returning to the foot of the hill by the stepped path and turning north, you descend to an area dense in the ruins of superimposed buildings and temples. In earliest times this area was dedicated to Hera, the goddess whose vengeance pursued Leto until she finally settled on Delos to give birth to the two divine twins. Hera was most likely venerated here in a largely propitiatory fashion: even though her role was an obstructive one in the story of Apollo and Artemis, the great goddess was nonetheless never to be overlooked, and it was appropriate to mark her cult here with an imporant sanctuary. The venerable, 6th century BC **Temple of Hera** is immediately to the north— just beyond a broken altar on a platform—consisting of a south-facing entrance with two standing columns, and an east wall of fine construction in marble which rises almost imperceptibly in the centre. The interior floor is now missing, but reveals the solid base of what has been identified as a preceding, late **Geometric period temple** below, constructed with wood and mud-brick elements, which remains in effect enshrined by the later temple. The building is firmly identified by the dedication to Hera of numerous vases and terracotta figurines found here.

The Sanctuaries of Serapis and of the Syrian gods

To the north and west opens a large area known as the **Terrace of the Foreign Deities**—testimony to the cosmopolitan nature of the population of Delos in the last period of its mercantile prosperity during Late Hellenistic and Roman times. The Heraion now became surrounded by the sanctuaries of new, imported divinities—Egyptian Serapis to the south and west, and Syrian divinities to the north. The popularity of Serapis—a curious, composite or syncretic divinity, typical of the multi-cultural world of the Hellenistic age—derived from the fact that he was believed to have the powers of healing and of prophecy.

The **Serapeion** is an extensive complex which must have grown rapidly during the course of the 2nd century BC. Numerous inscriptions here testify to Athenian patronage in its construction. It comprised two colonnaded courts, several temples to Serapis, Isis and Anubis, altars, inscriptions and *ex votos*—its haphazard growth indicated by the fact that the complex has few right-angle corners, no over-riding alignment and little axial organisation. The long trapezoid court below the polygonal retaining wall of the Heraion is divided length-ways by a sacred **avenue**, in Egyptian style, which was lined with altars and crouching sphinxes (a couple at the south end of the western line survive), leading to a small temple set at an angle to the axis. The narrow, north end of this court abuts another paved area bounded on the south and partly on the west by an Ionic portico and surrounded by small temples and sacred rooms. The two most conspicuous temples are: to the *north*, a **Temple of Serapis** from the first half of the 2nd century BC built partly in a bluish marble with a *poros*-stone wall coated with stucco at the rear; and to the *east*, on a higher level above a ledge of natural rock, a

Temple of Isis whose **marble pedimented façade** has been pleasingly reassembled. Against its back wall is a statue of the goddess, probably dedicated by Athenians as an *ex voto*: a low fence closed off the *naos*, over which the head of the statue (now missing) would have been visible from outside. Lower down, directly in front of the temple, is an **incense altar** the upper part of which is decorated with four pieces of marble in the form of horns.

To the north—grander still in dimensions and conception than the Serapeion—lies the **Sanctuary of the Syrian gods**, Hadad and Atargatis, whose cult was also introduced here in the early 2nd century BC. Its beginnings would have been small and private, but by the end of the century it was made 'official' under the aegis of an Athenian high priest. In the process, Atargatis became identified with Aphrodite.

The original entrance to the Syrian sanctuary was by means of the stepped street which is visible rising steeply up to the terrace from the west: the path today does not respect the original enclosures and passes directly north from the Serapeion into the back of what was only a lateral courtyard of the Syrian sanctuary: after 25m it descends to the main terrace. Running north/south, on the left, was a long colonnade which would have been plastered and painted originally: in an *exedra* just left of its centre is an area of **pavement with a mosaic inscription** commemorating the benefaction of an Athenian named Phormion. To the right (*east*) is the sanctuary's **small theatre** (with 12 rows of seats accommodating 400–500 spectators) in which sacred rites were performed, protected from view by walls and an internal portico on three sides which surrounded the space. Sacred fish were kept in a tank in the sanctuary.

The grandeur of these two sanctuaries gives a sense of the wealth of the island's immigrant merchants; while their enclosed, inward-looking architecture speaks of a different cultic world from the open sanctuaries of the older Greek gods.

The area of the Inopos

The stepped path which descends to the west leads down to a large public cistern—the **Inopos reservoir**—cut into the rock, and now filled with fig trees, terrapins and frogs. At the north end marble steps led down to the water level which was regulated by a series of overflow holes. It collected the fugitive and variable waters of the Inopos torrent which drained from a source on the slope of Mount Kynthos and flowed intermittently down to the Sacred Lake and the Bay of Skardana. A curious Delian tradition imagined that its waters came from the Nile, an association perhaps endorsed by the resemblance of the local agama lizards to small crocodiles. A small terrace lined with bench-seats overlooked the cistern from the north and must have constituted a cool and pleasant meeting place to sit and converse.

Detour. On the opposite side, south of the reservoir, are the ruins of the '**Samothrakeion**', dedicated to the Samothracian Cabiri, who became increasingly identified with the Dioscuri twins in the late Hellenistic mind. The sanctuary is built on two terraces. On the upper level stood the 4th century BC Temple with a curiously asymmetric Doric portico. On the lower level was a circular altar of the 2nd century BC for offerings. To the right hand side are the foundations of a **monument to Mithridates Eupator**, king of Pontus (120–63 BC), with two Ionic columns and a frieze of medallions depicting his generals and allies.

A street runs between the Inopos Reservoir and a row of shops to the east: between two of the shops is an alley, with a bench carved with dedicatory inscriptions to Serapis, Isis and Anubis on its front edge. At the end of the alley is a staircase leading to the ruins of '**Serapeion B**', marked by several small 'horned' altars. The small temple is placed in the northwest corner of the court, facing south.

The main street continues, bearing left in front of the House of the Inopos (*see below*). On the left beyond the reservoir and the Shrine of the Nymphs to its west— a small circular building in marble, dedicated by the Pyrrhakides family—is 'Serapeion A', the oldest and most intimate sanctuary of Serapis on the island. Its temple stood facing west on a stepped basement in a paved court, between two small porticos; under its *naos* is a rectangular crypt, reached by a staircase and supplied with water by a conduit. Opposite the temple front is a meeting room with marble benches, on carved supports, round all four sides bearing **inscriptions** of dedication to Serapis, Isis and Anubis. On the surface of the bench on the west side has been carved a 12x12 chequer-board for playing games.

In this area are three of the finer Delian houses: to the *north* of Serapeion A is a house of curious design with a simple, perfectly preserved mosaic floor in three colours, on which stands the one and only column the house appears to have had, set at an odd angle to the floor-plan suggesting that it may belong to an earlier phase of the building than the floor. To the *east*, behind a **street façade** in beautifully dressed marble, is the '**House of the Inopos**', built around a central court with peristyle on two sides. There are eleven large, unfinished, monolithic marble columns which lie, where they were found, in an adjacent room. These can perhaps only be explained by some interruption in the construction or redesigning of the house which was never again resumed. The method of delivery of these massive columns into this very circumscribed space is a mystery. Further downhill to the east the pathway passes the '**House of Hermes**', an elaborate, four-storey dwelling of the late 2nd century BC, partially restored: only a part of three storeys exists today. The house takes its name from a number of herms found on the site.

The entrance is by a narrow hallway; immediately to left are the **latrines**, with carefully sloping water channels for drainage; at the end of the hall on the left is the **bathroom** proper with a terracotta bathtub still in place. The Doric **peristyle court** surrounds a marble *impluvium*: in the blank south wall is a cut made into the live rock with a slit deep into the left. There must have been a weak water source here in Antiquity which drained into the cistern, and was marked probably by a domestic shrine to the nymphs in the aedicule to the right. In the opposite (*north*) wall a wide marble doorway leads into the **main reception room** with two subsidiary rooms leading out from it. On the east side of the court a small **dining-room** still preserves a **painted plaster decora-**

tion, imitating marble plaques. Steps lead up to the upper floor, with similar configurations of interconnecting rooms.

Further to the west is a small, late 4th century BC **sanctuary of Aphrodite**, consisting of a temple surrounded by a number of smaller, ancillary sacred buildings. Beyond this point, paths return either to the museum (*right*) or to the embarkation mole (*left*).

SOUTH OF THE HARBOUR

Along the shore to the south of the Sacred Harbour, a series of **magazines** or **warehouses**, have their backs to the Theatre Quarter. They would have opened on to a quay bordering one of the five basins of the Commercial Harbour (whose outlines can be distinguished when the water is still). All have substantial marble thresholds for the fixing and locking of gates: one has a well-preserved peristyle court in its interior. Further south is the line of the **city wall** running down to the sea, followed by a second group of magazines. There was no conspicuous communication between these warehouses and the Theatre Quarter behind them—an indication possibly that much of Delos's commerce was essentially a transit trade. The blocks of buildings which follow are divided by streets running parallel to the sea or at right angles to it; each has a central court surrounded by large structures used as bonded warehouses. A typical example is the '**Magazine of the Columns**'. The building adjoining it has a fine marble basin in its vestibule. One hundred metres further south are the remains of a shoreside **sanctuary of the Dioscuri**, protectors of seamen, dating in all probability from the end of the 6th century BC.

Approximately 800m beyond, following an indistinct path, is the Bay of Fourni, sheltered from the north winds by a rocky promontory on which are the ruins of a Sanctuary of Asklepios which, as a refuge frequented primarily by the sick, was founded at a safe distance from the centre of the town. It consists of three buildings in a line. The northernmost is a pro-style Doric temple with four columns; beyond is a large hall constructed with granite blocks, with a door on its east side—probably an '*abaton*' or infirmary; and finally the Propylaia to the sanctuary, paved in white marble.

RHENEIA

To the west of Delos, at a distance of less than a kilometre stretches the lower half of the island of Rhéneia. The Rhevmatiari Islets lie in the channel between the two islands, making the crossing between the main islands narrower still. The archaeological interest on Rhéneia lies mostly in the northern part of the island which is joined to the lower portion by an isthmus less than 100m across. The ancient settlement was around the bay of Aghia Triada on the west coast. On the north side of the bay are the interesting remains of a **Sanctuary of Hercules**, dating from the late 2nd century BC, which were brought to light in 1900 together with a statue of the hero. An impressive and curious rectangular building in the sanctuary possesses some beautiful decorative elements: on its east side is a deep, semicircular tank with a water-spout in the form of a shell, and a delightful floor **mosaic depicting swimming dolphins**.

Of greatest archaeological significance, however, is the extensive **area of necropolis** on the east coast, opposite Delos. This was in effect the cemetery of Delos in the centuries following the sacred prohibition of death and burial on the island after the purification of 426 BC. The purification involved the exhumation of all previous graves on Delos and their transference all together to a prepared **purification pit** on Rhéneia. This is the rectangular enclosure located below the church of Aghia Kyriakí on the eastern shore. This pit, which was excavated in the last years of the 19th century, was predictably a gold-mine for archaeological studies because it contained an unprecedented quantity and variety of pottery dating from Geometric times up until the early 5th century BC: it is this valuable assemblage which constitutes the collection of the Mykonos Archaeological Museum.

The area further to the south along the coast continued to be used as the cemetery for Delos after 426 BC. A large number of tombs, altars, sarcophagi, and several hundred carved *stelai* and inscriptions have been unearthed in this area. In the midst is an underground **two-level complex of loculi tombs**, entered by means of a staircase and central corridor. The hills to the north were intensively cultivated in antiquity with farmsteads belonging to the sanctuary on Delos. On the northernmost tip of the island is the stepped base of an ancient monument.

Given the difficulty of organising transportation to Rhéneia, a visit to the Museum in Mykonos, which contains all the objects of value which come from this large area, represents an easier and perhaps more revealing option for the visitor.

PRACTICAL INFORMATION

Delos (Dhílos) area 3.53sq.km; Rhéneia (Rínia) area 14.0sq.km; no permanent resident population on either island; max. altitude 112m (Delos), 136m (Rhéneia). **Port Authority of Mykonos** T. 22890 22218.

ACCESS

Access to Delos is only via Mykonos. A selection of boats leave every morning (weather permitting), except Mon, from 9am onwards from the old harbour of Mykonos (south mole) and make the 30 minute crossing to Delos, returning regularly up until 3pm when the site closes. Average cost: €12 r/t. Rhenia, which is also a restricted archaeological area, can only be visited by making private arrangements with a caïque service in Mykonos.

LODGING

Commercial lodging is not available on either island since they are both archaeological sites in their entirety. See 'Mykonos:Lodging' for suggestions.

FURTHER READING

Delos has been meticulously excavated already for over a century and a quarter by the French Archaeological mission in Greece, and much of the most authorative material on the island is produced by the Ecole Française d'Athènes. Their '*Guide de Délos*' is exemplary and exhaustive,

INDEX

GLOSSARY OF CLASSICAL TERMS

acroterion—an ornamental fixture on the extremity of a building

aedicule—a niche, or small shrine, often with architectural frame

agora—a large public space, mainly given over to commerce

ambo—the pulpit or lectern of an Early Christian church

amphora—a tall, terracotta receptacle with handles for transportation of liquids

antron—a cave or grotto

apotropaic—having the power to turn away evil

Archaic period—the 7th and 6th centuries BC

bothros—a pit or trench

Cabiri—divinities associated with 'Mystery' sanctuaries, esp. Samothrace

cavea—the hemicycle of seats accommodating the public in a theatre

crepis—the platform of a temple

Daphnephoria—the sacred rite of bearing laurels in honour of Apollo at Delphi

diadumenos—sculptural figure of an athlete tying the

ribbon of victory on his head

Dioscouri—Castor and Polydeuces, twin sons of Zeus; saviours and protectors of mariners

dromos—an entrance passage or axial approach to a tomb or building

ecclesiasterion—an assembly room

emblema—the intricately-detailed central panel of a floor-mosaic

exedra—an architectural protrusion or a free-standing structure of semicircular form

Geometric period—the 10th–late 8th centuries BC

Hellenistic period—era of, and after, the campaigns of Alexander the Great, c. 330–c. 150 BC

hestiatorion—a building for ritual dining

impluvium—the water-catchment area in the centre of an ancient house, above a cistern

in antis—(of columns) set between projecting side-walls or wings (antae) of a building

isodomic—(of masonry) constructed in parallel courses of neatly-cut rectangular blocks

kouros—the statue of a nude, male figure

lebes—a cauldron-shaped vessel

loculi—compartments, or excavated rectangular tombs, for burial

naiskos—a small free-standing shrine

naos—the central, inside chamber of a temple

oculus—(in architecture) a circular aperture for letting in light from above

oikos—a house (here on Delos) a religious building which is not actually a temple

orchestra—the circular, or partially circular, floor of a theatre reserved for the chorus and for dance

palaestra—a building for the performance of physical exercise and gymnastics

paraskenia—the entrances or wings to the side of the stage-structure in a theatre

peribolos—the perimeter wall of a temple precinct

poros stone—any soft limestone of porous composition used for construction

pronaos—the front vestibule of a temple, preceding the naos

propylaia—the monumental gateway at the entrance to a sanctuary or street

pro-style—(of a building) with an entrance or portico of free-standing columns

prytaneion—the 'town-hall' or office of the chief(s) of an ancient city

sema—a mound or cairn, or a place marked out as 'special' or sacred

skene—the stage structure of a theatre

stoa—a long, covered colonnade open on one side and closed (by shops or offices) on the other

stele—a carved tablet or grave-stone

synthronon—the rising, concentric rings of seats for the clergy in the apse of a church

temenos—the sacred area surrounding an altar and temple, defined by the peribolos

templon—the screen in a church which closes off the sanctuary

tesserae—the small pieces of coloured stone or glass-paste which compose a mosaic

theke—a place of burial

thyrsos—a stick or wand, wreathed in ivy or vine leaves, associated with Dionysos

xystos—a covered colonnade for running and exercise, affording protection from the weather

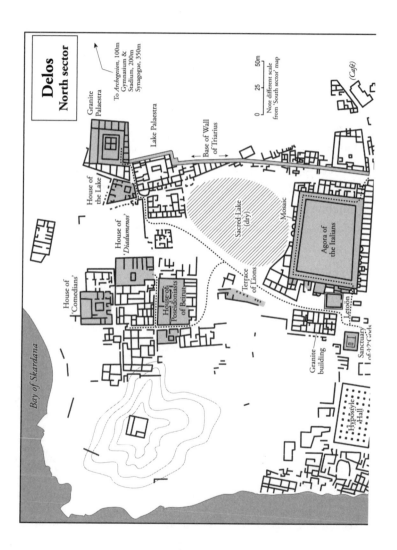

Delos
North sector

To *Archegesion*, 100m
Gymnasium &
Stadium, 200m
Synagogue, 350m

Granite
Palaestra

Lake Palaestra

Base of Wall
of Triarius

House of
the Lake

0   25   50m

Note different scale
from 'South sector' map

(Café)

House of
'Diadumenos'

Sacred Lake
(dry)

Mosaic

Agora of
the Italians

House of
'Comedians'

House of
Poseidoniasts
of Beirut

Terrace
of Lions

Bay of Skardana

Granite
building

Letöon

Sanctuary
of the Gods

Hypostyle
Hall

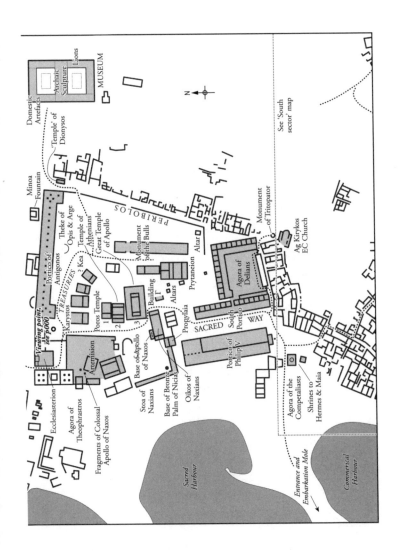

MUSEUM

Lions

Archaic Sculpture

Domestic Artefacts

N

Temple of Dionysos

See 'South sector' map

Minoa Fountain

Theke of Opis & Arge

Temple of Athenians

Great Temple of Apollo

Temple of Apollo

Monument of the Bulls

Ag Kirykos EC Church

Portico of Antigonos

TREASURIES

2 Kea

Karystos

Poros Temple

1

2

3

Altar

Prytaneion

Monument of Tritopator

Agora of Delians

Viewing point, see p.000

Artemision

Base of Apollo of Naxians

Building Γ

Altars

Propylaia

SACRED

South Portico

WAY

Ecclesiasterion

Agora of Theophrastros

Fragments of Colossal Apollo of Naxos

Stoa of Naxians

Base of Bronze Palm of Nicias

Oikos of Naxians

Portico of Philip V

Agora of the Competaliasts

Shrines to Hermes & Maia

Sacred Harbour

Entrance and Embarkation Mole

Commercial Harbour

PERIBOLOS

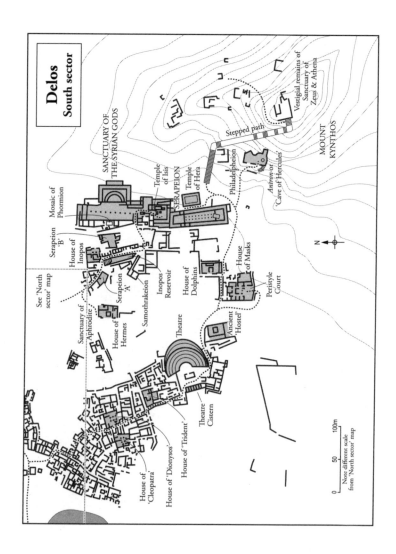

Delos
South sector

SANCTUARY OF THE SYRIAN GODS

Vestigial remains of Sanctuary of Zeus & Athena

Stepped path

MOUNT KYNTHOS

Temple of Isis

Temple of Hera

SERAPEION

Philadelpheion

Antron or 'Cave of Hercules'

Mosaic of Phormion

Serapeion 'B'

House of Inopos

See 'North sector' map

Serapeion 'A'

Inopos Reservoir

House of Dolphins

House of Masks

N

Sanctuary of Aphrodite

Samothrakeion

House of Hermes

Peristyle Court

Theatre

Ancient 'Hostel'

House of 'Cleopatra'

House of 'Dionysos'

House of 'Trident'

Theatre Cistern

0   50   100m

Note different scale from 'North sector' map